Asia and Pacific

Resource Directories previously published

Third World Resource Directory
Latin America and Caribbean

Asia and Pacific

A Directory of Resources

Compiled and edited by
Thomas P. Fenton
and
Mary J. Heffron

ORBIS BOOKS
Maryknoll, New York 10545

Zed Books Ltd.
57 Caledonian Road
London N19BU

The Catholic Foreign Mission Society of America (Maryknoll) recruits and trains people for overseas missionary service. Through Orbis Books Maryknoll aims to foster the international dialogue that is essential to mission. The books published, however, reflect the opinions of their authors and are not meant to represent the official position of the society.

Graphics Credits: Asian Bureau Australia (113), *Asian Rights Advocate/* Lithograph by Tomiyama Taeko (93, 107), *Bulletin of Concerned Asian Scholars* (16, 43), Rachel Burger/CPF (48), *China Talk* (59), Community Aid Abroad (34), *Pacific Research* (9), *Pandanus Periodical* (79), *Praxis* (101), *Tok Blong SPPF* (109). From Data Center Graphics Collection.

Manufactured in the United States of America

Library of Congress Cataloging in Publication Data

Fenton, Thomas P.
Asia and Pacific.

Includes index.
1. Asia—Bibliography. 2. Pacific area—Bibliography.
3. Asia—Audio-visual aids—Catalogs. 4. Pacific area—Audio-visual aids—Catalogs. 5. Asia—Societies, etc.—Directories. 6. Pacific area—Societies, etc.—Directories. I. Heffron, Mary J.
II. Title.
Z3001.F46 1986 [DS5] 016.95 85-21842
ISBN 0-88344-528-X (pbk.)

British Library Cataloguing in Publication Data

Fenton, Thomas P.
Asia and Pacific: a resource directory.

1. Information services—Asia 2. Asia—Bibliography 3. Information services—Pacific Region 4. Pacific Region—Bibliography
I. Title II. Heffron, Mary J.
950′.07 Z3001

ISBN 0-86232-635-4
ISBN 0-86232-636-2 Pbk

To Santiago Alonzo, a former political prisoner in the Philippines, whose words to his wife speak, as well, to those who desire to be one with the peoples of Asia and the Pacific in their struggle for justice:

How cruel and inhuman
so high, so huge
this partition between us
for so long
but in spirit, we are one
as always
bound by unbreakable bonds
of love and longing for justice.

Contents

Where Can I Find . . . ?

"Where can I find information on the former U.S. police training programs in Asia?" a researcher on Central America recently asked.

In 1974 Congress had banned all "public safety" aid after discovering that the American teaching programs for Thai, Korean, Taiwanese, Laotian, (south) Vietnamese, and Filipino police included torture techniques. In 1985 efforts were being made to gain Congressional approval for a resumption of police training aid—this time for Central American countries.

How times have changed.

Without hesitation, I snatched up the galley copy of the Asia and Pacific resource directory and handed it to the researcher. For an hour she jotted down names of U.S. and foreign organizations, documentary films, articles, and pamphlets. Finally, she looked up and exclaimed, "What an amazing yellow pages!"

I agree. This resource directory is truly the "yellow pages" for peace and justice in Asia and the Pacific.

For an office like ours, the where-can-I-find queries can seem endless. "Where can I find documentation on child labor in Southeast Asia?" a TV producer asks. "Where can I find statistics on the wages at Asian textile mills?" a union organizer asks. "Where can I find a speaker on the growing U.S. militarization in the Asian Pacific?" a church leader asks. That is why my colleagues and I at the Asia Resource Center are grateful to Tom Fenton and Mary Heffron for putting together this prized tool.

Now we can "let our fingers do the walking"—and you can, too.

Why should you care about what it is going on in Asia and the Pacific? Ronald Reagan provided one reason during his 1984 election campaign: "That is where the future of the world lies."

Almost unnoticed, the Asia and Pacific region has become tense and unpredictable over the last decade. Superpowers are deploying and stockpiling nuclear weapons there at an alarming rate. Military-controlled governments are building ominous arsenals to keep themselves in power. The Soviets and Americans are engaging in a naval arms race unmatched elsewhere. And the U.S. Pacific Command is brazenly and provocatively "playing war games" that have involved over half of the U.S. naval forces and those of Japan, south Korea, Thailand, the Philippines, Australia, and New Zealand.

The region is fraught with potential flashpoints: hot wars in Kampuchea and Afghanistan are fueled by superpower rivalries; U.S. soldiers are said to be engaged in combat missions for the Marcos military dictatorship; and unanswered questions surround the downing of Korean Airlines flight 007.

Added to these are two related facts. First, the United States carries on most of its economic trade with Asian countries ($136 billion in 1982, or thirty percent). Second, the United States operates its largest overseas bases from the Pacific. Thus, as Pacific Commander-in-Chief William Crowe stated in 1984, "The U.S. has unequivocally reaffirmed that it is in Asia, that it plans to stay there, and that it will stay in a big way."

If this growing militarization makes you feel gloomy, please, quickly let your fingers walk through these lists and lists of organizations, publications, books, and audiovisuals. See for yourself how citizens throughout Asia and the Pacific are challenging the notion that more arms means more security. Find out for yourself why they look for their futures to improved education, housing, income distribution, and food production—not to M-1 tanks or MIG-25 fighters or police training or war games.

After fifteen years of education and action about Asia and the Pacific, I have come to realize that bald facts and figures rarely move us from our easy chairs. Rather, it is human stories mixed with a broader message that captivate our attention. As Vietnamese friends used to tell me, "Tell them we want this war to end because we are *people,* not statistics or kill ratios."

For this reason, I am especially energized when I thumb through this directory and see so many materials by Asian and Pacific peoples. It is heartening to see the number of resources they have produced.

Filipinos are now producing films calling for an end to U.S. support for the Marcos regime and the removal of U.S. bases at Clark and Subic Bay; South Koreans are writing about how 40,000 U.S. troops and 175 nuclear warheads on their already tense peninsula have turned their land into a nuclear tripwire; Pacific Islanders, Japanese, and New Zealanders are all campaigning for a nuclear-free Pacific; and Thai activists are creating gripping slideshows on the slums of Bangkok.

And all this has developed during the past decade!

Organizing around Asian and Pacific issues has unquestionably come a long way since the beginning of the Vietnam War, when few even knew where Vietnam was. But we are still weak in drawing inter- and intra-regional connections.

We, in the industrialized West, must understand how violations of labor rights in the Philippines, Taiwan, Korea, Thailand, and other countries are related to the problems of workers, farmers, and taxpayers here. We need to work closely with Atlantic disarmament advocates to rid the Pacific of the 350 nuclear warheads already deployed there. And we need to study the forgotten "secret" CIA wars fought years ago in Laos, Kampuchea, and the Philippines in order to understand the covert wars of today in Central America.

This directory lets our fingers step over national and regional barriers to build the international understanding and cooperation we desperately need.

We are also weak at distributing our educational resources. Most of the organizations in this book do not have budgets for high-gloss, high-cost publicity. With financial support for Asian and Pacific work so painfully limited, we need help in notifying teachers, journalists, students, religious leaders, and community activists—everyone—about the resources we are producing.

This resource directory surely will be a boon to our business of peace-making.

Onward,

JACQUI CHAGNON,
ASSOCIATE DIRECTOR,
ASIA RESOURCE CENTER

Foreword

Why is the Third World "third"?

Most people of the First World would answer, "because the majority of its citizens are poor and oppressed, exploited by their governments and by their nations' rich and powerful families." Their answer would be correct—but not complete.

For most people of the First World have given no thought at all to the policies of their own governments that have supported, fostered, and—in some cases—instituted the poverty and oppression of the Third World. This is often done in the name of "national security," although its real purpose is to protect the government, not the people.

The Philippines, my country, is a shining example.

Since 1984, our dictator, Ferdinand E. Marcos, has been the object of sharp criticism from the U.S. press and officials of the U.S. government who have all but told him to step down from office to "preserve democracy."

But the press and these officials do not reveal how Washington has pushed policies on the Marcos government that have kept wages down and poverty up, favored foreign over domestic investment, and allowed the widespread corruption and abuse so bitterly criticized today. Nor do they acknowledge the fact that U.S. officials knew that martial law would be declared in the Philippines one year before it actually was.

The U.S. government approved of martial law for various reasons. It was convinced, for one thing, that "Marcos would continue to improve the position of foreign investment" (W. Scott Thompson, *Unequal Partners,* pp. 150–1). It also reasoned that they believed that "military bases and a familiar government in the Philippines are more important than the preservation of democratic institutions" (Staff Report, U.S. Senate Committee on Foreign Relations, Feb. 18, 1973).

The liberation of the Third World is in the hands of its people. We must find our own way to freedom and development. Support from the outside must be just that: support. We will not be dictated to by representatives of either the First or the Second World.

Those who wish to aid us in our pursuit of radical social, political, and economic change will find this directory to be a unique and invaluable tool. The resources it contains provide analyses of Third World affairs that the mainstream press and government officials ignore or suppress.

Radical change in the Third World will come about only if progressive forces unite in common purpose. Here, too, this resource directory makes a commendable contribution, for it encourages the forging of links among organizations and concerned people everywhere who support our struggle for liberation.

José W. Diokno, Chairman,
Free Legal Assistance Group
(FLAG) of the Philippines

Preface

This directory of resources on Asia and the Pacific is one in a series of twelve volumes on Third World regions and issues that is being compiled by the Data Center's Third World Resources project.

OBJECTIVES

Our aim in compiling this and all the other resource guides in the twelve-volume series is to meet five objectives:

1. *To strengthen the ties among organizations that oppose the injustices in foreign military and economic intervention in the Third World by helping to dismantle the institutional, issue-related, and regional barriers that now divide these groups.*

Educators and activists who take a critical stance toward the impact of foreign intervention in Third World affairs are unnecessarily divided from one another and thus not as effective or as mutually supportive as they could be. They are divided institutionally, by issue orientation, and by region.

Institutional walls separate church workers from academics, community organizers from researchers, and social studies teachers from political activists. Third World Resources seeks to breach these institutional walls by publicizing the work of groups in all of these categories and by promoting their resources through a worldwide network of Third World-related, progressive organizations.

Ironically, *issues* also drive wedges among activist organizations. Nuclear groups work on freeze issues, but fail to fully appreciate the urgency of the work of Korea-support organizations and vice versa. While this might make some sense tactically and while this focus of energies is perfectly understandable given the demands on the time of organizers, the lack of a network of mutually supportive, progressive organizations clearly limits the impact of their work.

By putting people in touch with people—whatever the issue that may be their prime concern—Third World Resources encourages better cross-fertilization of ideas and plans. This results in more effective joint action and less duplication of effort in the production of education and action resources.

Regional barriers also fragment the resistance movement. Transnational corporations are—unfortunately—years ahead of their critics in realizing the need to have near-instantaneous communication across regional and national boundaries. Critics need to appreciate as well the importance of the broadest and quickest possible interchange of information and of plans for action.

Third World Resources transcends *regional* boundaries by including in this directory and in all its publications education- and action-oriented resources from all over the world. In this international aspect of our work we are helped by an international board of advisors and by our affiliation with Interdoc, the international network of research and documentation centers.

2. To legitimize and give equal time to alternative points of view on Third World affairs in general and on the involvement of the United States and other major powers in the Third World in particular.

In the United States critical analyses of the devastating impact of foreign public and private interests in the Third World are woefully underrepresented on library shelves across the country, and the challenging voice of oppressed Third World peoples is heard only as a whisper in the media and in classrooms. We suspect that this criticism applies equally well to other major industrialized powers.

—Yet analytical and educational work of this nature is being done. The array of resources presented in this directory testifies to that fact. This work *must* be publicized more widely.

—Critical Third World voices *are* crying out for justice. These voices *must* be magnified.

Commenting on the *Third World Resource Directory* the director of the Third World Studies Center in Manila has said: "The publication of the resource directory is truly heartwarming, for it tells us abundantly that in America not everyone has been silent or silenced and that many are laboring to explain the links between the behavior of the U.S. government and multinationals and the problems that we face in our own countries."

The purpose of the present directory is to publicize the efforts of those who are explaining these links and to make certain that the victims of interventionism by U.S. and other powers have an opportunity to tell their story.

3. To promote the education/action resources of Third World-related organizations in a sustained, focused, and professional manner.

Data Center president Fred Goff described this problem in his foreword to the *Third World Resource Directory:* "All too often the limited resources available to these [progressive] organizations are consumed by the processed of producing a given book, pamphlet, newsletter, or film. Little energy or money remains for adequately publicizing these resources."

Anyone who has worked in solidarity and anti-intervention organizations knows how true this observation is. Even when the desire is there to reach beyond the institutional, issue-related, and regional barriers described above, the energy and financial resources that this outreach demands are too often just not there. This results in the under-utilization of available resources and—perhaps even worse—the waste of limited time and money in the production of redundant resources.

Third World Resources furthers the promotional outreach of progressive organizations by focusing its energies on *identifying* and *acquiring* resources from all over the world on regions such as Asia and the Pacific, on *evaluating* and *describing* the resources in a careful, nonrhetorical fashion, on *presenting* them in an attractive, readily accessible format, and on *publicizing* the work of these organizations to a broad audience of educators, researchers, librarians, and political activists.

4. To put in the hands of researchers and organizers in the Third World comprehensive guides to Third World-related organizations and educational resources in other parts of the world.

Data Center president Fred Goff spoke to this problem as well: "Researchers and organizers in the Third World have learned from experience that information critical to their struggle for social justice—information about the realities of power in their own countries—is often available only here in the United States" (foreword, *Third World Resource Directory*).

Third World Resources responds to this need of activists and educators in the Third World by providing them with handy sourcebooks of annotated descriptions and comprehensive lists of organizations, books, magazines, films, and other resources on a wide variety of Third World regions and Third World-related issues. The *Third World Resources* newsletter keeps these references current, and the Third World Resources documentation clearinghouse at the Data Center assures easy access to the entire collection of resources from anywhere in the world.

5. To direct concerned citizens in First World countries to the books, periodicals, audiovisuals, and other resources they need to study in order to take informed and effective action to correct injustices in the ways their governments and businesses treat Third World nations and peoples.

This directory and the others in the twelve-volume set are designed to offer immediate answers to the questions concerned citizens ask: How can I find out more about the impact of transnational corporations in Southeast Asia? What can I read to help me understand what is happening in the Middle East? What steps can I take to help people in the Philippines or to stop U.S. intervention in Central America? Where can I rent a good educational film on South Africa?

THIRD WORLD RESOURCES

The present directory and the entire twelve-volume set of resource directories update and expand the resources we presented in the *Third World Resource Directory* (Orbis Books, 1984) and complements the two other facets of our Third World Resources project: a quarterly newsletter and resource guide, and a clearinghouse of Third World-related resources.

Quarterly Newsletter and Resource Guide

The project publishes a sixteen-page quarterly newsletter with notices and descriptive listings of organizations and newly released print, audiovisual, and other educational resources from and about the Third World.

Each issue of the newsletter contains a unique four-page resource guide that provides comprehensive coverage of one particular region or issue. This resource guide is available at discounts for bulk distribution.

Clearinghouse of Third World-related Resources

In order to insure the widest possible access to the resources gathered in the course of our work on the resource directories and newsletter we catalog and integrate all incoming information and materials into the library collection of the Data Center where they can be used by the hundreds of journalists, teachers, community organizers, and others who visit the center's public-access library each year. The materials are also available to the center's national and international network of Search Service clients.

In addition, bibliographical data on all of the resources are stored in a computerized data base to facilitate identification and retrieval of cross-referenced resources and to pave the way for future on-line access to this unique storehouse of critical information.

APPRECIATION

The work of Third World Resources is sustained by friends all over the world who give generously of their time, money, resources, kind words, and encouragement. This directory and all our efforts are dedicated to them with heartfelt thanks for their support.

We acknowledge in a special way the assistance of the Data Center and of our international advisory council and the financial contributions from these organizations: Committee for East Asia and Pacific of the National Council of Churches (USA), Division of Overseas Ministries of the Christian Church (Disciples of Christ), Maryknoll Fathers and Brothers, Board of Global Ministries of the United Methodist Church, Asia Division of the United Church of Canada, United Church of Christ Board of World Ministries, and the United Presbyterian Church (USA).

Introduction

The table of contents (above) is a guide to the overall structure of this directory. Each of the six chapters opens with an introduction that describes the format and contents of the particular chapter.

In this introduction we offer comments on the format and content of the directory as a whole.

FORMAT

This directory updates and expands the resources in the Asia and Pacific chapter of the *Third World Resource Directory* (Orbis Books, 1984). That chapter (pp.60–88), as well as cross-referenced entries throughout the 1984 directory, should be consulted for complementary annotated lists of organizations and their resources on Asia and the Pacific.

We have tried to include complete descriptive and ordering information for every citation in the present directory. Addresses for the organizations, publishers, and distributors appear either in the organizations index in the back of the book or with the actual entry. The bold face page numbers in the organizations index refer to the entries that contain addresses.

CONTENT

Our comments on the content of this directory and on the resources themselves fall into three categories: definitions, scope, and political orientation.

Definitions

Our treatment of Asia and the Pacific is confined geographically to the regions themselves. We have omitted the real and urgent concerns of the peoples of those regions who are now living in North America, Europe, and other areas outside of Asia and the Pacific. We refer you to the sources of information in each of the six chapters of this directory for indirect references to resources on these issues.

West Asia (or, more popularly, the Middle East) will be covered in the resource directory on the Middle East that is forthcoming from Orbis Books in 1987.

Scope

In compiling this directory we endeavored to identify and acquire resources from Asia- and Pacific-related organizations in all parts of the world. We acknowledge, however, that we still have a long way to go toward our goal of making the resources truly international in origin.

We realize that we have probably overlooked significant organizations and resources in Europe, Asia, the Pacific, and elsewhere and that certain areas (such as South Asia) have not been given the attention they deserve. We ask that you take into account the severe limits of time, funds, and geographical location with which we work and that you work with us to expand the reach of future editions of this directory.

In each of the chapter introductions below we call attention to the fact that organizations were selected for inclusion in this directory because their work is predominantly focused on Asia and the Pacific. In an effort to keep the directory to a modest size we had to omit organizations whose focus is much broader than just those two areas. No directory on Asia and the Pacific is complete without the education and action resources of international organizations such as Amnesty International and Clergy and Laity Concerned. Therefore, we urge you to consult the references given in the information sources section of each chapter for the names and addresses of complementary organizations such as these.

Political Orientation

In the preface to the *Third World Resource Directory* we described the resources in that directory as—by and large—"partisan and biased in favor of the radical analysis we have advanced. Most illuminate the problems and prospects of Third World peoples from the point of view of the 'powerless.' Many are critical of the role that the American government and U.S.-based transnational corporations play in the Third World." (Our concern in that directory was with U.S. relationships to Third World peoples and nations. In this and future directories we intend to broaden the references to include other major political powers.)

Since the resources in the present directory are similar in character to those in the 1984 directory, we shall restate the summary points we made about the radical analysis that informed our choice of resources:

Our study, training, and experience lead us to conclude that:

- reforms in the system are not enough; the crying need is for radical (that is, fundamental) changes;
- change will come about through struggles (though not necessarily violent ones) between the "powerful" and the "powerless";
- U.S. institutional power in the Third World often frustrates genuine development.

Our survey of hundreds of educational resources about the Third World has us concerned that most resources—and certainly the bulk of what we are exposed to in the media—ignore this "radical" analysis in favor of one that:

- stresses reforms;
- addresses all Americans as if they are rich and powerful and describes all in the Third World as if they are poor and powerless;
- judges all struggles for radical social change to be Soviet-inspired and, therefore, to be opposed.

In openly admitting our political orientation in this way we feel it is necessary to underline at the same time the fact that political biases are woven into most—if not all—education and action resources on the regions and issues we are covering, whether those resources be left-wing, right-wing, or moderate in character. One cannot describe or analyze events in the Third World without betraying the lines of a political belief system regarding the means and pace of social change, the causes of social unrest, the allegiance owed one's government, and so forth.

We have been straightforward about our own partisanship because we believe strongly that it is important for all to identify, evaluate, and admit to the biases that inform their analysis of and decisions regarding Third World affairs. Educators and librarians especially should be diligent about calling attention to the political biases in all of the resources on their desks and shelves—not just those that are alternative or radical in orientation.

In compiling a directory of alternative resources we are not advocating the wholesale substitution of one body of thought for another. For one thing, as a careful study of the resources in this directory will demonstrate, there is no "one body of thought" on the varied and numerous issues treated below—even though we have grouped them all under an alternative and politically radical umbrella. For another, a confession of one's political biases is not necessarily to be equated with a lack of appreciation for or openness to the truth in other points of view.

Our overriding aim is to promote the critical and responsible study of the alternative points of view represented in the resources in this directory along with consideration of all other descriptions and analyses of Third World affairs.

1

Organizations

This chapter is divided into three parts: annotated entries, supplementary list of organizations and sources of additional information.

Each **annotated entry,** includes: organization's name; address; telephone number; organization's self-description (in quotation marks); keyword descriptions of the organization's political and religious affiliation; focus (first geographcal, then according to issues); activities; resources; and periodicals.

The keywords were selected by the organizations themselves and are intended to provide a quick overview of each organization's work. The descriptors are neither all-inclusive nor scientific.

If the name of a periodical stands alone, this means that the magazine, newsletter, or newspaper is fully annotated in the periodicals chapter below. Otherwise pertinent descriptive information accompanies the citation.

Organizations in the **supplementary list** (pp. 15–18) are grouped under these headings: General Asia and Pacific; China; East Timor; Indonesia; Korea; Malaysia and Singapore; Philippines; and Thailand. Entries in this section include the organization's name and address.

Note that the three appendixes supply additional organizational information.

The **information sources** section (pp. 18–19) provides the names of directories and guides that contain the names of other organizations related to Asia and the Pacific.

All of the organizations and periodicals in this chapter are listed in the appropriate indexes at the back of this directory.

ANNOTATED ENTRIES

Asia Monitor Resource Center, 444–46 Nathan Rd., 8–B, Kowloon, Hongkong. Tel: (3) 855319.

"AMRC is a small, independent, and nonprofit information group based in Hongkong and set up in the belief that accurate, comprehensive, and accessible information should not remain exclusively in the hands of the rich and powerful. Since 1976, AMRC has been gathering, organizing, and disseminating information on the effects of foreign economic, military, and political influence on the lives of people in Asia."

FOCUS: International • Asia. Investment • trade • aid • militarism • transnational corporations • labor • political economy • corporate responsibility • working conditions in the chemical and agribusiness industries.

ACTIVITIES: Research and writing • documentation • public-interest information center • networking.

RESOURCES: Publications • reports • library search service • research services.

PERIODICAL: *Asia Labour Monitor.*

SPECIAL PROJECT: Study of chemical hazards in Asian agriculture and manufacturing.

Asia Resource Center, P. O. Box 15275, Washington, DC 20003. Tel: (202) 547–1114.

"In October 1984 the Southeast Asia Resource Center consolidated its three offices (Berkeley, New York, Washington) into one based in Washington, D. C., and changed its name to Asia Resource Center to reflect its broadened focus on the entire Asia region. The ARC carries back issues of the *Southeast Asia Chronicle.*"

FOCUS: International • Asia and Pacific. Human rights • militarism, peace, disarmament • nuclear arms and energy • foreign aid and trade • women • labor • political economy • international awareness • national liberation struggles • transnational corporations • social justice • native peoples • food, hunger, agribusiness.

ACTIVITIES: Popular education • research and writing • media • networking • constituency education • congressional testimony • documentation and information • justice and peace ministries • distributor of literature and audiovisuals.

RESOURCES: Speakers • audiovisuals • study-action guides • research services • curriculum guides • reports • books and literature • back issues of the *Southeast Asia Chronicle.*

PERIODICAL: *Asia Insights.* 3 issues/year. Newsletter.

Asia Society, 725 Park Ave., New York, NY 10021. Tel:(212) 288–6400.

"The Asia Society is a nonprofit educational organization dedicated to deepening American understanding of Asia and stimulating thoughtful trans-Pacific discourse in conjunction with the Committee on Teaching about Asia, a standing committee of the Association for Asian Studies."

FOCUS: Asia and Pacific. History • culture and customs • arts • international relations • geography.

ACTIVITIES: Political economy • constituency education • research and writing • intern programs • library services • media relations program • networking workshops and seminars • performing arts program • educational aids for high-school teachers.

RESOURCES: Speakers • audiovisuals • literature • publications • bookstore • study guides • consultant services • library.

PERIODICAL: *Focus on Asian Studies.*

Asian Bureau Australia, 173 Royal Parade, Parkville, Victoria 3052, Australia. Tel: 347-8595.

"ABA is a research-based social action organization concerned with the relation of Australians with Asian and Pacific peoples. ABA works in association with church, development, justice, and mission organizations in Australia, Asia, and the Pacific."

RELIGIOUS AFFILIATION: Christian.

FOCUS: Asia and Pacific. Human rights • militarism, peace, disarmament • women • labor • social justice • native peoples.

ACTIVITIES: Research and writing • solidarity work • networking • constituency education • library services • documentation and information • publisher • distributor of literature • workshops and seminars • justice and peace ministries.

RESOURCES: Research services • books and literature • library • calendar.

PERIODICAL: *Asian Bureau Australia Newsletter.*

Canada Asia Working Group, 11 Madison Ave., Toronto, Ontario M5R 2S2, Canada. Tel: (416) 924-9351.

"The Canada Asia Working Group is a coalition of Canadian churches, Asian community groups, and interested individuals working for human rights and social justice in Asia and Canada. The group is engaged in human rights advocacy, research and documentation, and education and support to groups in Asia."

RELIGIOUS AFFILIATION: Human Rights Advisory Council, Canadian Council of Churches.

FOCUS: Asia and Pacific. Human rights • militarism, peace, disarmament • nuclear arms and energy • foreign aid and trade • women • labor • national liberation struggles • transnational corporations • social justice • food, hunger, agribusiness.

ACTIVITIES: Popular education • political action • research and writing • solidarity work • intern programs • media • networking • constituency education • legislative action • policy-oriented research and writing • documentation and information • workshops and seminars.

RESOURCE: Speakers.

PERIODICAL: *Canada Asia Currents.*

Center for International Policy, Indochina Project, 236 Massachusetts Ave., NE, Suite 505, Washington, DC 20002. Tel: (202) 546-8181.

"The Center for International Policy is a nonprofit education and research organization concerned with U.S. foreign policy toward the Third World and its impact on human rights and human needs. The center's Indochina Project seeks ways to develop a better understanding of the countries of Indochina and their relations with the United States."

FOCUS: Asia and Pacific. Human rights • militarism, peace, disarmament • foreign aid and trade • women • labor • political economy • social justice • native peoples • food, hunger, agribusiness.

ACTIVITIES: Research and writing • media • networking • publisher • workshops and seminars • constituency education • legislative action • policy-oriented research and writing • congressional testimony • documentation and information.

RESOURCES: Speakers • research services • reports.

PERIODICAL: *Indochina Issues.*

Center for the Progress of Peoples, 48 Princess Margaret Rd., 1st floor, Kowloon, Hongkong. Tel: (3) 7145123.

"The center's aim is to support and serve justice efforts in Asia. The work of the CPP has five characteristics: it is religiously inspired; independent; Asia-oriented; directed to development, justice, and peace issues; and geared to the needs of grass-roots and action groups, while also cooperating with concerned professionals and scholars."

FOCUS: Asia and Pacific. Human rights • militarism, peace, disarmament • nuclear arms and energy • women • labor • international awareness • transnational corporations • social justice.

ACTIVITIES: Research and writing • solidarity work • networking • film/slideshow producer • documentation and information • publisher • workshops and seminars • distributor of literature and audiovisuals • justice and peace ministries • advocacy • training • developing educational aids.

RESOURCES: Audiovisuals • literature • study-action guides.

PERIODICAL: *Asia Link.*

Christian Conference of Asia, 480 Lorong 2 Toa Payoh, Singapore 1231. Tel: 2553671.

"CCA is a conference of 110 churches and national councils from sixteen countries in Asia. An organ of cooperation among these in the common task of serving the mission of Christ in Asia, the conference seeks to fulfil its objective by getting members together, through their representatives, to think and act together in their witness and service to Asian communities. The most common characteristics of the majority of the people in Asian nations are poverty and deprivation of many kinds. Therefore the objective of the thinking—in theological and other areas—and of the action that CCA facilitates is to help the churches to help one another to make their witness and service relevant to this Asian reality."

RELIGIOUS AFFILIATION: Christian (non-Roman Catholic).

FOCUS: Third World general • Asia and the Pacific. Human rights • militarism, peace, disarmament • nuclear arms and energy • foreign aid and trade • women • labor • international awareness • national liberation struggles • transnational corporations • social justice • native peoples • food, hunger, agribusiness • implications of all the above issues for Christian mission in Asia and for all Christians and churches in Asia.

ACTIVITIES: Research and writing • networking • constituency education • publisher • workshops and seminars • overseas project support • justice and peace ministries • foreign service.

RESOURCES: Study-action guides • books and literature • consultant services.

PERIODICAL: *CCA News.* 12 issues/year. Newsletter.

Christian Institute for the Study of Justice and Development, 345–78 Pyongchang-dong, Chongro-ku, Seoul 110, Korea. Tel: 353–7154.

"CISJD engages in research and analysis of issues such as industrialization and social change in Korea, sociopolitical functions of new religions in Korea (including the 'Unification Church'), poor women in service sectors, and the effects on the labor movement of Korea's system of subcontracted workshops. The center disseminates the results of its studies through publications, consultations, and public education."

RELIGIOUS AFFILIATION: Ecumenical.

FOCUS: Third World general • Asia and Pacific • Korea (North and South). Human rights • militarism, peace, disarmament • nuclear arms and energy • foreign aid and trade • women • labor • national liberation struggles • transnational corporations • people's struggle for human rights and democratization in the Third World • Third World theology • Korea-U. S. relations • North-South Korea relations, including reunification.

ACTIVITIES: Popular education • research and writing • solidarity work • networking • constituency education • policy-oriented research and writing • library services • press service • documentation and information • publisher • distributor of literature • workshops and seminars • overseas project support • labor counseling.

RESOURCES: Research services • books and literature • consultant services • library • news clipping service.

PERIODICAL: *History and Christianity.* 3 issues/year. Magazine.

Church Coalition for Human Rights in the Philippines, P.O. Box 70, 110 Maryland Ave., NE, Washington, DC 20002. Tel: (202) 543–1094.

"The aims of the coalition are: (1) to educate church people about the situation in the Philippines and how it connects with U. S. policies and corporate interests; (2) to stimulate responsible action among U. S. Christians in terms of challenging specific policies contributing to injustice in the Philippines; (3) to advocate in Congress and in other spheres of influence on behalf of justice issues affecting the Filipino people."

RELIGIOUS AFFILIATION: Ecumenical.

FOCUS: Philippines. Human rights • militarism, peace, disarmament • nuclear arms and energy • foreign aid and trade • women • labor • political economy • international awareness • national liberation struggles • transnational corporations • social justice • native peoples • food, hunger, agribusiness • U. S. military bases • foreign intervention in the Philippines • the role of the church in struggles for liberation.

ACTIVITIES: Popular education • political action • research and writing • solidarity work • intern programs • media • networking • film/slideshow producer • constituency education • legislative action • policy-oriented research and writing • congressional testimony • press service • documentation and information • publisher • distributor of literature and audiovisuals • justice and peace ministries.

RESOURCES: Speakers • audiovisuals • books and literature • consultant services • papers and documents from an ecumenical conference on the Philippines.

PERIODICAL: *Philippine Witness.* 6 issues/year. Newsletter.

Church Committee on Human Rights in Asia, 5253 N. Kenmore, Chicago, IL 60640. Tel: (312) 561-4953.

"The committee publicizes news of current events and stories of the struggles for human rights in Korea, Taiwan, and the Philippines. Through its monthy publication, *Asian Rights Advocate,* the CCHRA calls for concerted actions by U.S. citizens in solidarity with the people in the movements for justice in the three countries."

FOCUS: South Korea • Taiwan • Philippines. Human rights • militarism, peace, disarmament • nuclear arms and energy • foreign aid and trade • women • labor • political economy • international awareness • national liberation struggles • transnational corporations • social justice • native peoples • food, hunger, agribusiness.

ACTIVITIES: Popular education • political action • research and writing • solidarity work • intern programs • media • networking • publisher • distributor of literature and audiovisuals • workshops and seminars • overseas project support • constituency education • legislative action • congressional testimony • library services • documentation and information • justice and peace ministries.

RESOURCES: Speakers • audiovisuals • study-action guides • research services • curriculum guides • books and literature (from other organizations) • consultant services • library.

PERIODICAL: *Asian Rights Advocate.*

Committee for a New Korea Policy, 221 Central Ave., Albany, NY 12206. Tel: (518) 434-4037.

"The Committee for a New Korea Policy works in support of human rights, a reduction of military tensions, and the right of Koreans—North and South—to decide their own future without outside interference or control."

RELIGIOUS AFFILIATION: Project of the Albany Friends Meeting (Quakers).

FOCUS: International • Asia and Pacific • Korea, North and South. Human rights • militarism, peace, disarmament • nuclear arms and energy • foreign aid and trade • women • labor • political economy • international awareness • national liberation struggles • transnational corporations • social justice • food, hunger, agribusiness • reconciliation.

ACTIVITIES: Popular education • political action • research and writing • solidarity work • media • networking • publisher • distributor of literature and audiovisuals • workshops and seminars • constituency education • legislative action • policy-oriented research and writing • documentation and information • slideshow producer • monthly radio program.

RESOURCES: Speakers • audiovisuals • study-action guides • research services • books and literature.
PERIODICAL: *Korea Pamphlet Series.*

East Timor Human Rights Committee, P.O. Box 363, Clinton Station, Syracuse, NY 13201.

"ETHRC was formed in 1980 to coordinate and develop public educational programs and resources on East Timor for a U.S. audience. ETHRC addresses the issues of human rights, hunger and relief assistance, political prisoners, and international rights regarding Indonesia's invasion and military occupation of East Timor."

FOCUS: East Timor. Human rights • international awareness • national liberation struggles • native peoples • food, hunger, agribusiness.
ACTIVITIES: Popular education • research and writing • media • networking • audiovisual producer • constituency education • policy-oriented research and writing • publisher • distributor of audiovisuals.
RESOURCES: Audiovisuals • books and literature.
PERIODICAL: *East Timor Update.*

Formosan Association for Public Affairs (FAPA), P.O. Box 15062, Washington, DC 20003. Tel: (202) 547-3686.

"FAPA's goals are: (1) to seek international support for the right of the Taiwanese people to determine the future of Taiwan (Formosa); (2) to protect and enhance the rights, interests, and welfare of Taiwanese communities throughout the world; and (3) to promote human rights, freedom, and democracy for the people of Taiwan."

FOCUS: Asia and Pacific • Taiwan. Human rights • nuclear energy • foreign aid and trade • labor • social justice • religious freedom • self-determination.
ACTIVITIES: Popular education • research and writing • media • networking • publisher • distributor of literature • constituency education • legislative action • policy-oriented research and writing • congressional testimony • documentation and information.
RESOURCES: Speakers • research services • books and literature • reports.
PERIODICAL: *FAPA Newsletter.* 12 issues/year (6 in English, 6 in Taiwanese). Newsletter.

Friends of the Filipino People, P.O. Box 2125, Durham, NC 27702.

"FFP is a nationwide organization that operates under four points of unity: (1) We seek an end to the U.S. government's support for the Marcos dictatorship; (2) We seek an end to the U.S. government's military and political intervention in the Philippines; (3) We condemn the long-standing domination of the Philippine economy by U.S. corporations, a factor which has been a major cause of continued poverty and underdevelopment of the Philippines; and (4) We support the Filipino people in their efforts to secure full independence and freedom in their country and social and economic justice in the United States."

FOCUS: Philippines. Human rights • militarism, peace, disarmament • nuclear arms and energy • foreign aid and trade • political economy • national liberation struggles • transnational corporations • food, hunger, agribusiness • labor • native peoples • women • harassment of Philippine political dissidents in the United States through the Extradition Treaty • U.S. military bases.

ACTIVITIES: Popular education • political action • research and writing • solidarity work • networking • audiovisual producer • legislative action • documentation and information • publisher • distributor of literature • distributor of audiovisuals.

RESOURCES: Briefs, fact sheets, and issue flyers • reports • speakers • audiovisuals • resource list.

PERIODICALS: *FFP Bulletin* and *FFP Update.* See *Philippine Research Bulletin* (p. 53 below).

Indonesian Documentation and Information Centre (INDOC), Postbus 11250, 2301 EG Leiden, Netherlands.

"Founded in 1979, INDOC is an independent, voluntary organization whose goal is to collect and disseminate information on social developments in Indonesia, with particular reference to human rights."

FOCUS: Indonesia. Human rights • women • labor.

ACTIVITIES: Research and writing • documentation and information.

RESOURCES: Books and literature • library • publications list.

International Committee for Human Rights in Taiwan, P. O. Box 45205, Seattle, WA 98105. Tel: (206) 365-8242. Also Postbus 91542, 2509 EC The Hague, Netherlands. Tel: (070) 85-85-89.

"The committee campaigns for the release of political prisoners in Taiwan, and supports the establishment of a free and democratic political system on the island."

FOCUS: Asia and Pacific • Taiwan. Human rights • political repression • censorship • political economy • international awareness • national liberation struggles.

ACTIVITIES: Political action • legislative action • congressional testimony • press service • networking • documentation and information • research and writing • publisher.

RESOURCES: Speakers • reports • literature.

PERIODICAL: *Taiwan Communiqué.*

KDP (Union of Democratic Filipinos), P.O. Box 2759, Oakland, CA 94602. Tel: (415) 547-6818.

"Through seven chapters across the country KDP organizes in the Filipino community against discrimination and for democratic rights. Its activists also participate in the U.S.-based anti-Marcos movement. KDP uses an 'anti-imperialist revolutionary perspective' in its organizing work."

FOCUS: Philippine politics • U.S. Filipino community concerns.

ACTIVITIES: Popular education • political action • research and writing • solidarity work.

RESOURCES: Speakers • audiovisuals • books and literature.

PERIODICAL: *Ang Katipunan.*

Korean Resource Center, 1720 Oregon St., No. 10, Berkeley, CA 94703. Tel: (415) 486-8759.

"The Korean Resource Center is a community organization that provides educational programs, cultural activities, social services, and research assistance in order to develop the following: critical consciousness of the ever-increasing internal and external problems facing the Korean community; creative plans for solving these problems; innovative approaches to providing social services."

FOCUS: South Korea. Labor • national liberation struggles • Third World community (Korean).

ACTIVITIES: Popular education • political action • solidarity work • constituency education • library services • workshops and seminars • distributor of literature and audiovisuals.

RESOURCES: Speakers • audiovisuals • literature • library.

PERIODICAL: *Korean Resource Center Newsletter.* 4 issues/year. Newsletter.

Midwest China Center, 308 Gullixson Hall, 2375 Como Ave., St. Paul, MN 55108. Tel: (612) 641-3233.

"The Midwest China Center is a not-for-profit coalition of upper Midwestern institutions and individuals representing religious, educational, business, civic, and cultural concerns. The center informs, educates, and builds mutually beneficial relationships between upper Midwesterners and the Chinese people."

FOCUS: China • Asia and Pacific. Human rights • militarism, peace, disarmament • nuclear arms and energy • foreign aid and trade • women • labor • political economy • international awareness • national liberation struggles • transnational corporations • social justice • native peoples • food, hunger, agribusiness.

ACTIVITIES: Popular education • research and writing • intern programs • media • networking • publisher • distributor of literature • workshops and seminars • constituency education • library services • press service • documentation and information • audiovisual producer.

RESOURCES: Speakers • audiovisuals • study-action guides • research services • curriculum guides • books and literature • consultant services • library • reports.

PERIODICAL: *Midwest China Center Newsletter.* 3 issues/year. Newsletter.

Nautilus Pacific Action Research, P.O. Box 309, Leverett, MA 01054. Tel: (413) 549-1709.

"Nautilus is a public-interest research and education organization

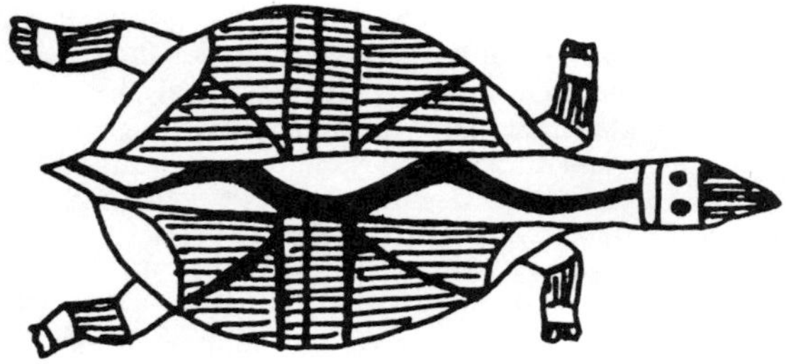

focused on U.S. involvement in the Asia-Pacific region. Founded in 1978, NPAR aims to produce high-quality yet popularly accessible reports and books particularly on issues of nuclear trade and energy development, militarism, and the growing nuclear arms threat in the Pacific."

FOCUS: Asia and Pacific. Militarism, peace, disarmament • nuclear arms and energy • foreign aid and trade.

ACTIVITIES: Research and writing • solidarity work • documentation and information.

RESOURCES: Speakers • research services • books and literature.

North American Coalition for Human Rights in Korea, 110 Maryland Ave., NE, Washington, DC 20002. Tel: (202) 546-4304.

"NACHRK brings together people and organizations actively supporting human rights and the restoration of democracy in Korea. The coalition gathers, analyzes, and disseminates information on political, economic, and social conditions in Korea; seeks to influence U.S. economic and military policy toward Korea; and mobilizes the North American people to aid those Koreans who suffer from human rights abuses."

RELIGIOUS AFFILIATION: Coalition of approximately 40 Catholic and Protestant faith groups.

FOCUS: Korea • Asia and Pacific. Human rights • foreign aid and trade • women • labor.

ACTIVITIES: Popular education • political action • congressional testimony • documentation and information • distributor of literature and audiovisuals.

RESOURCES: Audiovisuals • study-action guides • books and literature • weekly news reports available by telephone: (202) 546-NEWS • clipping service.

PERIODICAL: *Korea/Update.*

Pacific-Asia Resource Center, C.P.O. Box 5250, Tokyo International, Tokyo, Japan. Tel: 291-5901.

"PARC aims to build solidarity between the Japanese people and peoples over the world through the information it supplies and the communication it promotes. The center offers an alternative view of Asia and helps to break the monopoly of information exerted by transnational business and by the dominant sectors of Asian and world societies. PARC is especially concerned to give an accurate analysis of Japan itself and its relationship with Asia in the coming two years."

FOCUS: Third World general • Asia and Pacific • Japan. Human rights • militarism, peace, disarmament • nuclear arms and energy • foreign aid and trade • women • labor • political economy • international awareness • national liberation struggles • transnational corporations.

ACTIVITIES: Popular education • research and writing • solidarity work • documentation and information • audiovisual producer.

RESOURCES: Audiovisuals • research services • books and literature.

PERIODICAL: *AMPO: Japan-Asia Quarterly Review.*

Pacific Concerns Resource Center, P.O. Box 27692, Honolulu, HI 96827. Tel: (808) 538-3522.

FOCUS: Asia and Pacific. Human rights • militarism, peace, disarmament • nuclear arms and energy • political economy • national liberation struggles • native peoples.

ACTIVITIES: Popular education • political action • solidarity work • intern programs • networking • publisher • distributor of literature • documentation and information.

RESOURCES: Speakers • audiovisuals • books and literature.

PERIODICALS: *Pacific Bulletin* and *Pandanus Periodical.*

Pacific Studies Center, 222B View St., Mountain View, CA 94041. Tel: (415) 969-1545.

"PSC is a research and information center that focuses on U.S. foreign and defense policies, the activities of multinational corporations, and the political economy of Asia and the Pacific. Through its *Global Electronics Information Newsletter* the center hopes to establish an international network of researchers, journalists, and activists concerned about global production in semiconductors and similar industries. With this network PSC plans to develop a program of policy alternatives designed to make the electronics industry more responsive to the needs of workers in rich and poor countries alike."

FOCUS: Global • Asia and Pacific. Militarism, peace, disarmament • political economy • transnational corporations.

ACTIVITIES: Popular education • research and writing • publisher • workshops and seminars • policy-oriented research and writing • congressional testimony • library services • documentation and information.

RESOURCES: Speakers • research services • books and literature • library • reports.

PERIODICAL: *Global Electronics Information Newsletter.*

Philippine Resource Center, P.O. Box 40090, Berkeley, CA 94704. Tel: (415) 548-2546.

"PRC is a multipurpose clearinghouse of information, grass-roots organizing, and people-to-people exchanges between North America and the Philippines. The center publishes a monthy newsletter and occasional papers on the economic and political situation in the Philippines. PRC has conducted seminars for Filipino groups on the economic situation in the Philippines and arranged visits to the Philippines by persons and organizations from the United States."

FOCUS: Philippines. Human rights • militarism, peace, disarmament • nuclear arms and energy • foreign aid and trade • women • labor • political economy • international awareness • national liberation struggles • transnational corporations • social justice • native peoples • food, hunger, agribusiness.

ACTIVITIES: Popular education • political action • research and writing • solidarity work • media • networking • audiovisual producer • constituency education • legislative action • policy-oriented research and writing • library services • press service • documentation and information • publisher • distributor of literature and audiovisuals • workshops and seminars • overseas project support • organizing assistance to Filipino organizations • exchange of people between North America and the Philippines.

RESOURCES: Speakers • audiovisuals • study-action guides • research services • curriculum guides • books and literature • library.

PERIODICAL: *Philippine Report.* 12 issues/year. Newsletter.

Resource Center for Philippine Concerns, C.P.O. Box 1110, Tokyo 100–91, Japan. Tel: (03) 207–1481.

"RCPC is an Asia-based, alternative communications center focusing on human rights issues in the Philippines. The center serves as an international service agency committed to monitoring, documenting, and interpreting events in the Philippines and disseminating such information in Asia and throughout the world."

FOCUS: Asia and Pacific • Philippines. Human rights • militarism, peace, disarmament • foreign aid and trade • women • labor • political economy • international awareness • transnational corporations • social justice • native peoples.

ACTIVITIES: Research and writing • solidarity work • media • networking • audiovisual producer • policy-oriented research and writing • press service • documentation and information • publisher • distributor of literature and audiovisuals.

RESOURCES: Audiovisuals • research services • books and literature • consultant services • library • human rights information releases.

PERIODICAL: *Solidaridad II.*

Stanford Program on International Awareness and Cross-Cultural Education (SPICE), Stanford University, Lou Henry Bldg., Rm. 221, Stanford, CA 94305. Tel: (415) 497–1114.

"The central purpose of SPICE is the use of scholarly resources in international studies and education in cooperative endeavors with precollegiate educators to improve the international and cross-cultural dimensions of elementary and secondary schools. The major activities of the program are curriculum development and in-service education."

FOCUS: Global • international • Africa • Asia and Pacific • Latin America and Caribbean. Nuclear arms and energy • international awareness • international security and arms control • economics • trade and development.

ACTIVITIES: Distributor of literature and audiovisuals • workshops and seminars • teacher study tours abroad • summer institutes.

RESOURCES: Audiovisuals • curriculum guides and units • free catalog of resources.

PERIODICAL: *Colloquy.* 4 issues/year. Newsletter. Available from the Bay Area Global Education Program, c/o World Affairs Council, 312 Sutter St., San Francisco, CA 94108. Free to teachers.

Synapses, 1821 W. Cullerton, Chicago, IL 60608. Tel: (312) 421–5513.

"Synapses began as a conviction in the hearts of a few North American church workers who had spent time in Asia and Africa. We learned more clearly from brothers and sisters there how the policies and practices of banks, multilateral lending institutions like the World Bank, and the Pentagon set up overwhelming obstacles to genuine human and economic development. We felt it was important for North Americans to see through the eyes of sisters and brothers everywhere in order to make responsible decisions about life and work and struggle in North America."

FOCUS: Africa • Asia and Pacific • Latin America and Caribbean. Human rights • militarism, peace, disarmament • foreign aid and trade • women • labor • political economy • international awareness • national liberation struggles • transnational corporations • social justice • native peoples • food, hunger, agribusiness.

ACTIVITIES: Political action • research and writing • solidarity work • intern programs • networking • audiovisual producer • constituency education • policy-oriented research and writing • library services • documentation and information • distributor of literature and audiovisuals • workshops and seminars • justice and peace ministries • distributor of Nicaraguan coffee in the Chicago metropolitan area.

RESOURCES: Speakers • audiovisuals • library.

PERIODICAL: *Synapses Messages.*

TAPOL-UK, 8a, Treport St., London SW18 2BP, England. Tel: (01) 874-3262.

"TAPOL monitors and disseminates information about human rights abuse in the broadest sense in Indonesia and by Indonesia in East Timor and West Papua. We also campaign in various ways on related issues, for instance, monitoring death sentences, protecting the rights of West Papuan refugees, and soliciting legislators and other support for self-determination in East Timor and West Papua. TAPOL's material has worldwide circulation and its campaigns are developed on a worldwide basis as well."

FOCUS: Asia and Pacific • Indonesia • West Papua • East Timor. Human rights • militarism • national liberation struggles • native peoples.

ACTIVITIES: Political action • solidarity work • slideshow producer • publisher • distributor of literature and audiovisuals.

RESOURCES: Audiovisuals • books and literature.

PERIODICAL: *TAPOL Bulletin.*

Thai-American Project, 6565 Green Valley Circle, No. 306, Culver City, CA 90230. Tel: (213) 670-3477.

"The Thai-American Project serves as a linking organization for Thai in the United States and small nongovernmental organizations in Thailand undertaking works of development and social reform. The project provides financial support to these groups in Thailand: the Foundation for Children, the Foundation for Child Development (rural areas), the Center for Protection of Children's Rights (child labor), and the Slum Child Foundation. Project staff are interested in education and fundamental reform that would reduce the vulnerability of the poor."

FOCUS: Thailand. Militarism, peace, disarmament • foreign aid and trade • political economy • transnational corporations • social justice • food, hunger, agribusiness • issues affecting children, e.g., child labor.

ACTIVITIES: Research and writing • constituency education • documentation and information • overseas project support.

RESOURCES: Audiovisuals and literature • library of periodicals from small nongovernmental organizations in Thailand (English only) • occasional articles and brochures.

Third World Studies Center, University of the Philippines, Rm. 428, Palma Hall Bldg., Diliman, Quezon City, Philippines. Tel: 97–6061, ext. 783.

"The center was created in 1976 under the office of the dean of the College of Arts and Sciences of the University of the Philippines in response to the need for a program of studies and research that critically analyzes the problems of underdevelopment in the Third World and of the Philippines in particular. The TWSC maintains a resource collection and public reading room and carries on a program of research and publications, seminars and lectures, as well as audiovisual presentations."

FOCUS: Third World general. Human rights • militarism, peace, disarmament • nuclear arms and energy • foreign trade and aid • women • labor • political economy • international awareness • national liberation struggles • transnational corporations • social justice • native peoples • food, hunger, agribusiness.

ACTIVITIES: Popular education • political action • research and writing • intern programs • media • networking • audiovisual producer • constituency education • policy-oriented research and writing • library services • documentation and information • publisher • distributor of literature and audiovisuals • workshops and seminars • justice and peace ministries.

RESOURCES: Speakers • audiovisuals • study-action guides • research services • curriculum guides • books and literature • library • regular reports, papers, and books (catalog available).

PERIODICAL: *Kasarinlan.*

US-China People's Friendship Association (USCPFA), National Office, 2025 Eye St., NW, Suite 715, Washington, DC 20006. Tel: (202) 296–4147.

"The USCPFA is a nonprofit, tax-exempt, educational organization whose goal is to develop and strengthen friendship and understanding between the peoples of the United States and the People's Republic of China. We are North Americans of different viewpoints, from all walks of life, working in more than sixty-one affiliated chapters and organizing committees across the mainland and in Hawaii. The association is nonpolitical and nonpartisan."

FOCUS: People's Republic of China. International awareness • mutual understanding between the United States and China.

ACTIVITIES: Popular education • publisher • distributor of literature and audiovisuals • workshops and seminars • overseas project support • constituency education • congressional testimony • study tours program • exchanges.

RESOURCES: Audiovisuals • curriculum guides • books and literature • resources catalog.

PERIODICAL: *U.S.-China Review.*

U.S. Pacific Issues Network, 1203 Smith Tower, Seattle, WA 98104. Tel: (206) 343–7888.

"Objectives of the Network are: (1) to link the peoples' movements in the Pacific with U.S. disarmament, human rights, church, and environmental organizations in order to share resources and campaign strategies; (2) to support Pacific peoples' strategies for demilitarization and self-determination by educating the U. S. media, public, and governmental officials on crucial Pacific issues, and by promoting and coordinating political action and advocacy in North America; and (3) to facilitate and coodinate efforts of the network's regional offices and local support groups, and serve as a national resource center on Pacific issues."

FOCUS: Asia and Pacific. Militarism, peace, disarmament • native peoples.

ACTIVITIES: Political action • research and writing • solidarity work • media • networking • congressional testimony • library services • documentation and information • distributor of literature and audiovisuals.

RESOURCES: Speakers • audiovisuals • library • action alerts • congressional updates.

PERIODICAL: *U.S. Pacific Issues Network Newsletter.*

SUPPLEMENTARY LIST OF ORGANIZATIONS

GENERAL ASIA AND PACIFIC

In Australia:

Asia Partnership for Human Development, 154 Elizabeth St., 4th floor, Sydney, NSW 2000, Australia.

Australia Asia Worker Links, P.O. Box 264, Fitzroy, Victoria 3065, Australia.

In Canada:

South Pacific Peoples Foundation of Canada, 303–620 View St., Victoria, BC V8W 1J6, Canada.

Victoria International Development Education Association (VIDEA), 303–620 View St., Victoria, BC V8W 1J6, Canada.

In Hongkong:

Asian Regional Exchange for New Alternatives, 104–108 Baker St., A4, 2nd floor, G. Block, Hunghom, Kowloon, Hongkong.

Documentation for Action Groups in Asia (DAGA), 57 Peking Rd., 5th floor, Tsimshatsui, Kowloon, Hongkong.

In India:

Centre for Education and Documentation (CED), 3 Suleman Chambers, 4 Battery St., Bombay 400 039, India.

Christian Centre for Labour Concern, Osborne Rd., No. 67/2, Bangalore 560 042, Karnataka, India.

Indian Council for Research on International Economic Relations (ICRIER), 40 Lodi Estate, New Delhi 110 003, India.

Women's Research Centre, P–595 Purna Das Rd., Calcutta 700 029, India.

In Japan:

Center for Christian Response to Asian Issues, 2-3-18 Nishi-Waseda, Rm. 57, Shinjuku-ku, Tokyo 160, Japan.

In Malaysia:

International Organization of Consumers Unions, Consumer Information and Documentation Centre, P.O. Box 1045, Penang, Malaysia.

Sahabat Alam Malaysia (Friends of the Earth), 37 Lorong Birch, Penang, Malaysia.

In the Philippines:

BALAI Fellowship, 1043 Aurora Blvd., Quezon City, Philippines.

Office of Human Development, Federation of Asian Bishops Conference, P.O. Box EA-12, Ermita, Manila, Philippines.

Regional Council of Human Rights in Asia, 55 Third St., New Manila, Quezon City, Philippines.

In Sri Lanka:

Centre for Society and Religion, 281 Deans Rd., Colombo 10, Sri Lanka.

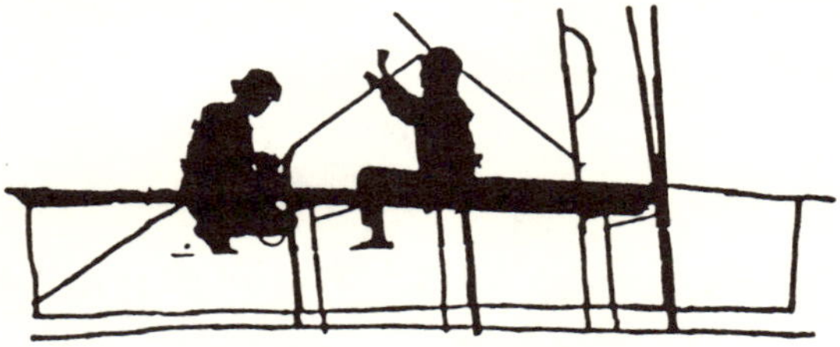

In Thailand:

Asian Cultural Forum on Development (ACFOD), P.O. Box 2930, Bangkok 10501, Thailand.

Ecumenical Coalition on Third World Tourism, P.O. Box 11-357, Bangkok 10110, Thailand.

In the United States:

Task Force on Militarization in East Asia-Pacific, c/o National Council of Churches USA, 475 Riverside Dr., New York, NY 10115.

Volunteers in Asia, P. O. Box 4543, Stanford, CA 94305.

CHINA

See Appendix 3.

EAST TIMOR

Indonesia East Timor Program, P.O. Box 1672, Peterborough, Ontario K9J 7S4, Canada.

See "East Timor: Unfinished Business," in *Southeast Asia Chronicle* 94 (June 1984). Page 25 lists organizations in eleven countries concerned with East Timor. Available for $2.50 from Asia Resource Center (Washington, D. C.)

INDONESIA

Indonesian Resources and Information Programme (IRIP), P.O. Box 190, Northcote, Victoria 3070, Australia.

Stichting Informatie Indonesie, Postbus 4098, 1009 AB Amsterdam, Netherlands.

KOREA

American Friends Service Committee, Korea Program, 1501 Cherry St., Philadelphia, PA 19102.

Association of Korean Christian Scholars in North America, P.O. Box 652, Princeton Junction, NJ 08550.

International Christian Network for Democracy in Korea, P. O. Box 904, New York, NY 10027.

Korea Support Committee, P.O. Box 11425, Oakland, CA 94611.

MALAYSIA AND SINGAPORE

FUEMSSO, c/o NUS, 461 Holloway Rd., London N7 6LJ, England.

PHILIPPINES

In the Philippines:

Ecumenical Center for Development, NCCP Bldg., 879 EDSA, Quezon City, Philippines.

Ecumenical Institute on Labor Education and Resources, P.O. Box SM 437, 2806 Metro Manila, Philippines.

Luzon Secretariat of Social Action (LUSSA), 48 Scout Tobias St., Quezon City 3008, Philippines.

Mindanao-Sulu Secretariat of Social Action (MISSSA), P. O. Box 508, Davao City, Philippines.

NASSA, 2655 F. B. Harrison St., Pasay City, Philippines.

Nuclear-Free Philippines Coalition, 2215 Pedro Gil St., Sta. Ana, Manila, Philippines.

Task Force Detainees of the Philippines, 214 N. Domingo St., San Juan, Metro Manila, Philippines.

Third World Movement against the Exploitation of Women, P.O. Box SM-336, Manila, Philippines.

Visayas Secretariat of Social Action (VISSA), Availa Bldg. No. 1, 3rd floor, Gen. Maxilom Ave., Cebu City, Philippines.

Elsewhere:

Alliance for Philippine Concerns, P.O. Box 19189A, Los Angeles, CA 90019.

Coalition against the Marcos Dictatorship, c/o 728 E. 37 Ave. (basement), Vancouver, BC V5W 1G1, Canada, and P.O. Box 173, Oakland, CA 94668.

Ecumenical Committee for Human Rights in the Philippines, 200–1955 W. Fourth Ave., B.C. V6J 1M7, Canada.

KSP (Komite ng Sambayanang Pilipino), P.O. Box 19195, 3501 DD Utrecht, Netherlands.

Montreal-Centre for Philippine Concerns, P.O. Box 232, Station Lafleche, St. Hubert, Quebec J4T 3J2, Canada.

Philippine Support Committee, 1346 Connecticut Ave., NW, Rm. 533, Washington, DC 20036.

Philippine Workers Support Committee, P.O. Box 11208, Moiliili Station, Honolulu, Hawaii 96828.

Philippines Research Center, 117 Davis Rd., Storrs, CT 06268.

Philippines Resource Centre, P.O. Box 5, 124 Napier St., Fitzroy, Victoria 3065, Australia.

Quebec–Philippines Solidarity Committee, 2692 Pie IX, Montreal, Quebec H1V 2E7, Canada.

THAILAND

Advance Media for Education and Development (AMED), 12/15 Convent Rd., Bangkok 10500, Thailand.

Coordinating Group for Religion in Society, 495/44 Soi Yoo Omsin, Jaransanitwong 40 Rd., Bangkok 10700, Thailand.

Justice and Peace Commission of Thailand, P.O. Box 4–67, Sam Sen Nai Post Office, Bangkok, Thailand.

Thailand Development Information Service, 128 Buckingham Palace Rd., 4th floor, London SW1W 9SH, England.

Union for Civil Liberty, 446 Soi Kiatchai, Asoke-Dindaeng Rd., Huaykwang, Bangkok 10301, Thailand.

For additional information on Asia- and Pacific-related organizations see:
Appendix 1: University Centers with Asia and Pacific Programs
Appendix 2: Christian Churches with Asia and Pacific Offices
Appendix 3: China Programs

INFORMATION SOURCES

The organizations included in this resource directory are for the most part regionally focused. Organizations such as Amnesty International and Clergy and Laity Concerned are not included because their interests and resources are broader than Asia and the Pacific. They do, however, include these regions in the course of their international work and should, therefore, be contacted. For information on such groups, see the bibliographies, guides, and reference books described below (pp. 34–40), as well as theses resources:

Human Rights Directory: Latin America, Africa, Asia. Washington, D.C.: Human Rights Internet, 1981. 244pp. $22.50. Indexes. Available from HRI, Harvard Law School, Pound Hall, Rm. 401, Cambridge, MA 02138.

This directory lists nearly four hundred organizations in Latin America and the Caribbean, Africa, the Middle East, and Asia and the Pacific concerned with issues of human rights and social justice. The directory also lists some seventy international groups based in Europe and North America, providing information on their objectives, activities, publications, and library holdings.

North American Human Rights Directory. Washington, D.C.: Human Rights Internet, 1984. 264pp. $30. Indexes. Available from HRI (address above).

This HRI directory lists nearly five hundred groups in the United States and Canada active in international human rights. It also includes listings of governmental and intergovernmental bodies with responsibility or concerns in this field. Each entry is fully annotated. Alphabetical and geographical listings for organizations are given, as is an index to their serial publications.

See also these two publications from Third World Resources:

Third World Resource Directory: A Guide to Organizations and Publications. Edited by Thomas P. Fenton and Mary J. Heffron. Maryknoll, N.Y.: Orbis Books, 1984. 304pp. $17.95, plus $1.50 shipping and handling. Illustrations, indexes. Available from Orbis Books, Maryknoll, NY 10545 or from Third World Resources, 464 19 St., Oakland, CA 94612.

The organizations section (pp. 4–16) of the Third World chapter should be consulted, along with the entire listing of organizations in the chapter on Asia and the Pacific (pp. 62–67). Cross-references in those sections direct readers to entries in other chapters (e.g., on women or human rights) that are related to Asia and the Pacific.

Third World Resources: A Quarterly Review of Resources from and about the Third World. 4 issues/year. Newsletter. 28cm. 16pp. $25/year (organizational subscription), $25/two years (individual subscription). Inquire for overseas rates. Subscriptions are available on a calendar-year basis only. Write: Third World Resources, 464 19 St., Oakland, CA 94612.

For additional annotated lists of organizations related to Asia and the Pacific, see the directory of information sources (pp. 545–56) in **Developing South Asia** (see p. 39 below), the lists of research institutes (pp. 79–88) and regional organizations (pp. 37–39) in **The Far East and Australasia 1984–85** (see p. 38 below), and the sections on each of the ethnic peoples in **Ethnic Inforamtion Sources of the United States** (see p. 39 below). These three books are annotated in the reference books section below.

See also standard library reference books such as the **Encyclopedia of Associations,** especially volume 4 on international organizations.

2

Books

This chapter is divided into three parts: annotated entries, supplementary list of books, and sources of additional information on books related to Asia and the Pacific. Annotated entries are divided into five sections: general books; bibliographies; catalogs, guides, and directories; curriculum guides and materials; and reference books.

Each **annotated entry** includes: author(s); title; place of publication; publisher; date of publication; number of pages; price; keyword description of format; description of content.

Books in the **supplementary list** (pp. 40–42) are grouped under these headings: Afghanistan; Bangladesh; Burma; China; East Timor; India; Indonesia; Korea; Malaysia; Pacific; Pakistan; Philippines; Singapore; Sri Lanka; and Vietnam. Entries in this section include author(s); title; place of publication; publisher; and date of publication.

The **information sources** section (pp. 42–43) provides the names of directories and guides that contain the titles of other books related to Asia and the Pacific.

All titles are integrated into the title index at the back of the directory. The addresses for all publishers and distributors appear in the organizations index. We have given the North American distributors for books published outside the United States. Readers in other countries should check with publishers for local distributors.

All books are paperback unless it is indicated that they are clothbound.

ANNOTATED ENTRIES

General

Association of Major Religious Superiors in the Philippines, Task Force Detainees Philippines (TFDP). ***Pumipiglas: Political Detention and Military Atrocities in the Philippines.*** Manila: Association of Major Religious

Superiors in the Philippines, Task Force Detainees Philippines, 1980. 132pp. $5. Illustrations, photographs. Available from the Philippine Resource Center (Berkeley, Calif.).

The Tagalog word *pumipiglas* is roughly translated to mean "struggling for freedom." Like other books published in the past by the TFDP, *Pumipiglas* chronicles the horrifying—yet hopeful—struggle of the Filipino people against political detention and military atrocities under the Marcos regime. *Pumipiglas* goes further, however, by narrating stories of struggles in the fields, factories, and tribal lands of the Philippines and by profiling those military officers who have been accused of the most brutal torture of alleged subversives.

The TDFP, organized by the Association of Major Religious Superiors of the Philippines immediately after the declaration of martial law in September 1982, monitors the arrests, detention, and abuses perpetrated by the military and provides aid to the victims and their relatives.

Bello, Walden, David Kinley, and Elaine Elinson. ***Development Debacle: The World Bank in the Philippines.*** San Francisco: Institute for Food and Development Policy and Philippine Solidarity Network, 1982. 280pp. $6.95. Foreword by Richard Falk. Tables, notes, bibliography, index. Distributed in the United Kingdom by Third World Publications, Birmingham, England.

Development Debacle offers a penetrating analysis of over six thousand pages of secret World Bank reports, memoranda, and assessments of the bank's program in the Philippines from 1970 to late 1981. The book's authors maintain that these documents "constitute straight-from-the-horse's-mouth evidence that the bank's programs have directly served U.S. strategic and corporate interests, supported authoritarian control by a brutal dictator, and worked against the welfare of the majority of the people in the Philippines."

Given the powerful role that the World Bank and other international financial institutions play in coordinating (or, in Richard Falk's words, "managing") economic relations between North and South, it is important to understand how they function and to see clearly the difference between their visionary rhetoric and their day-to-day practices. The World Bank personnel who leaked these revealing documents and the authors who interpreted them in very readable fashion pose questions that need to be asked and answered.

Budiardjo, Carmel, and Liem Soei Liong. ***The War Against East Timor.*** London: Zed, 1984. 272pp. $10.75. Photographs, maps, documents, diagrams, chronology, glossary, bibliography, index. Available in the United States from the Biblio Distribution Center (Totowa, N.J.). Also available from TAPOL-UK.

Drawing on classified Indonesian army documents, information from Fretilin (the national liberation movement of the people of East Timor), and a range of other sources, these two dedicated Indonesian activists document the Indonesian military's efforts to prevent the creation of a democratic independent state on Indonesia's borders. They trace the course of the war that followed Indonesia's invasion of the former Portuguese colony in 1975 and graphically describe the saturation bombing and starvation that has reduced the country's population by one-third since the invasion.

Caldwell, Malcolm, ed. ***Ten Years' Military Terror in Indonesia.*** Nottingham, England: Spokesman Books, 1975. 295pp. $5. Photographs, map, notes, appendix.

This powerful book opens with a photograph of an Indonesian soldier bayoneting a prisoner at his feet while two other men await their fate with hands bound behind their backs. The opening words are from British peace activist Bertrand Russell: "In four months, five times as many people died in Indonesia as in Vietnam in twelve years."

Though now more than a decade old the essays in *Ten Year's Military Terror* represent one of the few attempts to provide some background and critical analysis of the murderous reign of terror unleashed by the right-wing Suharto regime against upwards of one million Indonesians in late 1965 and early 1966.

The late Malcolm Caldwell begins the book with a summary essay on the international context in which Indonesia is situated. Essays by other contributors (such as Ernst Utrecht, Carmel Budiardjo, and Michael Klare) cover the politics and economics of Indonesia, the U.S. role in shaping and supporting the Suharto regime, and future prospects for the Communist Party of Indonesia (the PKI).

Chandler, David P., and Ben Kiernan, eds. ***Revolution and Its Aftermath in Kampuchea: Eight Essays.*** New Haven, Conn.: Yale University, Southeast Asia Studies, 1983. 321pp. $14. Maps, notes, lists of abbreviations, chronology (July 1942–October 1982).

This publication brings together essays by eight of the most knowledgeable students of Kampuchea: Anthony Barnett, Chanthou Boua, David Chandler, Ben Kiernan, Gareth Porter, William Shawcross, Serge Thion, and Michael Vickery. In studies that reach back into precolonial Cambodia and that are as up-to-date as the Heng Samrin government of 1982, these authors try to make some sense of the turbulent events that made Kampuchea "news" in the 1970s.

The editors acknowledge that this collection is, to an extent, eclectic: "There are serious gaps in what follows, particularly in the realms of economics, psychology, and foreign affairs." They succeed admirably, however, in accomplishing what they set out to do. They place the Kampuchea of the 1970s in a historical context that gives readers some insights into the origins of Pol Pot's Democratic Kampuchea and some reasons why that regime was driven from power by the Vietnamese-backed forces of Heng Samrin. Serge Thion's twenty-nine-page chronology is particularly helpful.

Charney, Joel, and John Spragens, Jr. ***Obstacles to Recovery in Vietnam and Kampuchea: U.S. Embargo on Humanitarian Aid.*** Boston: Oxfam America, 1984. 150pp. $5. Impact Audit Series No. 3. Preface by Laurence R. Simon. Map, photographs, glossary, choronologies, appendices, bibliography.

"American private voluntary organizations are being prevented by the United States government from carrying out humanitarian aid programs," writes Oxfam America's director of policy analysis in his preface to this short book. "Using the threat of criminal sanctions," Laurence Simon continues, "the Reagan administration seeks to turn such organizations into handmaidens of its foreign policy."

Obstacles to Recovery describes the way in which U.S. legislation prohibits or inhibits development assistance to the four countries that the U.S. State Department has labeled as "enemies": Cuba, North Korea, Kampuchea, and Vietnam. Concentrating their attention on the latter two countries, Charney and Spragens study the impact of Washington's "hostile policies" on the war-ravaged people of Indochina and on the private voluntary organizations themselves. Without absolving the governments of Vietnam and Kampuchea of responsibility "for the plight of their people," the authors plead with the U.S. government to accept its share of the blame for the present situation in Indochina and to begin to walk down the "road not taken": "the path of negotiation, reconciliation, and eventual respect and friendship" with Vietnam and Kampuchea.

Chomsky, Noam, and Edward S. Herman. ***Political Economy of Human Rights.*** 2 vols. Vol. 1: ***The Washington Connection and Third World Fascism.*** 441pp. $6.50. Vol. 2: ***After the Cataclysm: Postwar Indochina and the Reconstruction of Imperial Ideology.*** 392pp. $6.50. Boston: South End Press, 1979. Notes, illustrations, index.

Authors Chomsky and Herman set forth a dual focus for their powerful two-volume study of U.S. relations with the Third World: facts and beliefs.

"The basic fact," they say, "is that the United States has organized under its sponsorship and protection a neo-colonial system of client states ruled mainly by terror and serving the interests of a small local and foreign business and military elite." This fact, which they document in detail, is at odds with the belief "that the United States is dedicated to furthering the cause of democracy and human rights throughout the world, though it may occasionally err in the pursuit of this objective."

Both volumes draw heavily on Asian case studies to describe the realities of U.S. intervention in or support for repressive client states in the Third World and to illustrate the ways in which institutions, such as the media, "falsify, obscure, and reinterpret the facts [of this intervention and support] in the interest of those who dominate the economy and political system."

The authors admit that the picture that emerges from their exhaustive study is "a very grim one," but they take solace in the fact that "this system is not all-powerful, as millions of people learned from their own experience during the U.S. war in Indochina."

Christian Conference of Asia—Urban Rural Mission (CCA-URM). ***Minangkabau: Story of People vs. TNCs in Asia.*** Hongkong: CCA-URM, 1981. 154pp. $2. Illustrations, maps, photographs, bibliography.

The book takes its title from an Indonesian folk tale that expresses the hope and aspirations of people who struggle against the unjust demands of tyrannical oppressors. The Urban Rural Mission division of the Christian

Conference of Asia compiled *Minangkabau* in order to inspire people to action vis-à-vis transnational corporations (TNCs). For "in the final analysis," states CCA–URM secretary A. George Ninan, "it is the people—victims—who have to rise up and defend their rights, for the very process of such a rising up itself is a movement towards a just and creative society." Using case studies, *Minangkabau* describes in simple terms the motives and mechanisms of West German, Japanese, U.S., and other transnational corporations in Asia and then offers as counterpoint successful stories of resistance to the TNCs by industrial and agricultural workers in Malaysia, Hongkong, South Korea, and other countries in the region.

Christian Conference of Asia–Urban Rural Mission. ***Struggling to Survive: Women Workers in Asia.*** Hongkong: CCA–URM, 1983, 2nd ed. 162pp. $1, plus postage. Photographs, maps, illustrations, tables.

This short book contains stories of Asian women workers in five countries: Thailand, Malaysia, the Philippines, Sri Lanka, and Hongkong. Case studies describe the low wages, long working hours, and inhumane treatment that are the lot of these women. Each section opens with a short essay that puts the stories into a national and historical context.

Cumings, Bruce, ed. ***Child of Conflict: The Korean-American Relationship, 1943–1953.*** Seattle: University of Washington Press, 1983. 352pp. $22.50. Cloth. Figure, notes, index, bibliographical guide.

Based entirely on recently declassified archival materials relating to U.S. policy toward Korea in the early post–World War II period, this historical collection presents startling new analyses of the origins of the Korean War.

A lengthy introduction by Bruce Cumings, associate professor of international studies and political science at the University of Washington, and essays and commentaries by ten other historians and political scientists cover themes such as: the reasons for the division of Korea in August 1945, the guerrilla movement in South Korea during the late 1940s, U.S. policy in Korea as a test case of containment, the decision to march north of the thirty-eighth parallel, and the 1953 negotiations at Panmunjom.

In the concluding chapter, Jack Saunders, an archivist with the National Records Center, provides a thorough seventeen-page guide (written during the Carter administration) to the extensive archives on the U.S. occupation of Korea.

Drinnon, Richard. ***Facing West: The Metaphysics of Indian-Hating and Empire-Building.*** Minneapolis: University of Minnesota Press, 1980. 571pp. $20. Cloth. Illustrations, photographs, notes, bibliographical essay, index.

In this major investigation into the links between racism and American westward expansion, Richard Drinnon has his readers "tag along with European immigrants as they become citizens of the republic and push the American empire into the setting sun." "See what they do," Drinnon proposes, "and listen attentively to what they have to say, and then try to understand all that, as well as their unspoken convictions."

Convinced that "individuals are the living substance of history, the carriers and creators, sometimes, of the attitudes and ideas of their generations," Drinnon tells his tale in the prose and verse of a grab bag full of characters beginning with Thomas Morton battling the "Satanic hordes" of Pequot Indians in the Massachusetts Bay Colony, ranging through people like Jesuit Father John X. Finian, who searched the jungles of Burma for devilish communists, and ending up in the hamlet of My Lai where First Lieutenant William L. Calley was later to say: "We weren't [there] to kill human beings, really. We were there to kill ideology that is carried by—I don't know. Pawns. Blobs. Pieces of flesh. . . ."

Drinnon devotes over one-half of his study to U.S. expansionism in the Pacific and Asia.

Eisen, Arlene. ***Women and Revolution in Viet Nam.*** London: Zed, 1984. 294pp. $10.75. Map, glossary, photographs, notes, chronology, list of recommended readings and resource centers. Available in the United States from the Biblio Distribution Center (Totowa, N.J.).

In this sequel to a book she wrote in the waning years of U.S. intervention in Vietnam (*Women of Viet Nam* [San Francisco: Peoples Press, 1974]), Arlene Eisen offers a frank and unromantic assessment of the personal and societal situation of Vietnamese women since liberation in 1975.

"After the war with the United States ended," Eisen asks, "what happened in Viet Nam? What is the experience of women living in the southern provinces, once occupied by U.S. troops, now building a socialist society? How do they organize for change? How do women who once identified with the U.S. troops they serviced transform their consciousness and recover their dignity? . . . How does the Vietnamese experience compare with the experience of women facing wartime conditions without socialism? Or of women in colonizer, rather than colonized, countries?"

Women and Revolution situates these questions in the historical context of Vietnamese feudalism and patriarchy, French colonialism, and U.S. military aggression. Then, combining numerous interviews and her own historical research, the author presents facts about virtually all aspects of the lives of women in present-day Vietnam with the hope that these facts will "illuminate an ongoing discussion" of these and many other questions related to women's liberation and socialism.

Gale, Roger W. ***The Americanization of Micronesia: A Study of the Consolidation of U.S. Rule in the Pacific.*** Washington, D.C.: University Press of America, 1979. 352pp. $14.25. Maps, notes, tables, bibliography, index.

"The primary purpose of this study," states the author, is "to examine the political processes that have led to American control [of Micronesia] and which will determine its extent and longevity."

The book begins in the Marianas, the first islands in the Pacific to become subject to Western rule (in 1521), and sweeps up to the years immediately after World War II when the United States annexed Micronesia. Gale analyzes the consolidation of the territories into U.S. strategic plans for the Pacific and speculates about the lines of their future relationship with Washington.

The author's bibliography is especially useful because research and writing in this area have not been plentiful.

Girling, John L. S. ***Thailand: Society and Politics.*** Ithaca, N.Y., and London: Cornell University Press, 1981. 306pp. Cloth. Maps, notes, suggested readings, index.

Thailand: Society and Politics is a popularly written analysis of the political, economic, and social factors that have shaped recent Thai history. Girling's readable textbook is particularly useful for the background material it provides about the ebb and flow between democracy and right-wing bureaucracy in Thailand in the 1970s.

Before he became a senior fellow in international relations at the Australian National University (Canberra), John Girling spent fourteen years in the British Foreign Service dealing extensively with Thailand and its Asian neighbors.

Thailand: Society and Politics is one in a series of studies on the "politics and international relations of Southeast Asia" under the general editorship of Cornell University's George McT. Kahin. Recent titles in the series include: *Malaysia and Singapore: The Building of New States* by Stanley S. Bedlington, *Burma: Military Rule and the Politics of Stagnation* by Josef Silverstein, *The Army and Politics in Indonesia* by Harold Crouch, and *Indonesian Foreign Policy and the Dilemma of Dependence: From Sukarno to Soeharto* by Franklin B. Weinstein.

Griffen, William L. and John Marciano. ***Teaching the Vietnam War: A Critical Examination of School Texts and an Interpretative Comparative History Utilizing the Pentagon Papers and Other Documents.*** Montclair, N.J.: Allanheld, Osmun, 1979. 183pp. $6.50. Notes, index.

"For years," observe the authors of *Teaching the Vietnam War*, "many Americans have argued that we must learn from the Vietnam experience." "An obvious starting place," Griffen and Marciano say, "is in the schools." Thus they undertook this critical study of the ways in which the war in Vietnam has been treated in twenty-eight textbooks. Their aim: to help "all Americans who at some time in their schooling became miseducated by dishonest textbooks and do not want more of the same visited on their children."

The first half of *Teaching the Vietnam War* is a synthesis of the history of the war as it appears in the twenty-eight textbooks. This history is divided into three periods: (1) origins of U.S. involvement, (2) the Diem years (1954–63), and (3) escalation, "Vietnamization," and the end of the war. The second half of the book is a concise history of the same periods told in the authors' own words. The differences between the two portions of the book are striking. The authors—professors of education at the State University of New York at Cortland—close with a short essay on the social function of history textbooks at the secondary-school level.

Harrison, James Pinckney. ***The Endless War: Fifty Years of Struggle in Vietnam.*** New York: McGraw-Hill, 1983. 374pp. $8.95. Maps, notes, bibliography, index. Also from Collier Macmillan Publishers, London.

The absence of an "adequate and up-to-date explanation" of the war in

Vietnam inspired City University of New York professor James Harrison to try his hand "at a brief history and analysis." Harrison not only accomplished what he set his hand to, but he makes a unique contribution in fashioning a history of the Vietnamese revolution that concentrates "on the Vietnamese side of the events."

U.S. intervention and the role of other players such as France, Japan, China, and the Soviet Union are not ignored, but Harrison's "principal goal is to give some historical understanding of how the Communists took command of the Vietnamese Revolution and went on to defeat enemies so many times more powerful than they."

Hayes, Peter, Lyuba Zarsky, and Walden Bello. ***An American Lake: Militarism and the Nuclear Peril in the Pacific.*** Boston: South End Press, 1985. 400pp. $11. Maps, figures, index.

Based on four years of research, this well-documented study provides the first overview of U.S. weapons systems and military bases in Asia and the Pacific. In over thirty chapters the authors examine a range of issues, including the CIA and "sublimited war," nuclear war by the book, deployment of the Tomahawk missile, regional resistance movements, and security implications of U.S. disengagement from Pacific and Indian Ocean bases.

Part 3 of *An American Lake* explains the functions and interrelations among U.S. bases in Hawaii, Guam/Micronesia, Okinawa, the Philippines, Japan, South Korea, Australia/New Zealand and the South Pacific, and the Indian Ocean.

Herman, Edward S., and Frank Brodhead. ***Demonstration Elections: U.S.-Staged Elections in the Dominican Republic, Vietnam, and El Salvador.*** Boston: South End Press, 1984. 270pp. $8. Tables, appendices, footnotes.

The thesis of this book is that elections, such as those in the Dominican Republic in June 1966, Vietnam in September 1967, and El Salvador in March 1982, are "demonstration elections," that is, "elections organized and staged by a foreign power primarily to pacify a restive home population, reassuring it that ongoing interventionary processes are legitimate and appreciated by their foreign objects."

Herman and Brodhead examine in detail the three U.S.-sponsored elections cited above and expose them as public relations gestures that meet none of the criteria of integrity for free elections, such as, freedom of speech and organization, and the absence of coercion and fear on the part of the general population.

Chapter 3 deals with the "classic demonstration election . . . held under U.S. auspices in South Vietnam on September 3, 1967."

Hinton, William. ***Shenfan: The Continuing Revolution in a Chinese Village.*** New York: Vintage, 1984. 789pp. $10.95. Map, photographs, index.

In 1971 William Hinton returned to Long Bow—the Chinese village that he had lived in during the years following China's liberation in 1949 and that he had popularized in his classic book, *Fanshen*. As in *Fanshen*

Hinton paints a picture of China and its revolution in Shenfan that is deeply personal and unaffected. We walk and talk and sit with the author as he learns from old friends of the dramatic changes that have taken place in Long Bow and in China since the time of his last visit.

Hinton uses the Chinese word *shenfan*, which literally means a deep and thorough overturning of the soil, to suggest "all the painstaking effort peasants are willing to make once they own their own land" and to express "the spirit of the cooperative movement by means of which people, working together, try to fashion a new way of life on ancient fields."

Joseph, Paul. ***Cracks in the Empire: State Politics in the Vietnam War.*** Boston: South End Press, 1981. 362pp. $7. Charts, tables, glossary, notes, index.

In *Cracks in the Empire* Paul Joseph, a professor at Tufts University, advances the thesis that "the Vietnam War was not an accident but a logical outgrowth of the principles and interests guiding U.S. foreign policy" and that "the main beneficiary" of this foreign policy has been "the capitalist class within the United States."

Joseph studies various theoretical issues surrounding the nature of power and the political process in the United States in the context of one specific period during the U.S. intervention in Vietnam: from August 1967 through March 1968. In doing so he attempts to harmonize two realities: (1) the history of calculated intervention in Vietnam in pursuit of the basic principles of foreign policy, and (2) the "disagreement, conflict, and even chaos that exist within the state."

Though *Cracks in the Empire* is a "theoretical" work, Joseph writes in clear and accessible prose. Study of this unique analysis of U.S. involvement in Vietnam will certainly pay off in more sophisticated and more telling criticisms of U.S. intervention elsewhere in the world.

Kiernan, Ben, and Chanthou Boua, eds. ***Peasants and Politics in Kampuchea, 1942–1981.*** Armonk, N.Y.: M. E. Sharpe, and London: Zed Press, 1982. 401pp. $14.95. Preface by Wilfred Burchett. Glossary of Khmer terms, description of names and organizations, bibliography, index. Available in the United States from the Biblio Distribution Center (Totowa, N.J.).

Kiernan and Boua have compiled a unique collection of writings and translations (from the Khmer and French languages) intended to deepen an understanding of how this small, rural Southeast Asian country evolved its own revolutionary movement in the 1940s, was swept up in the holocaust of the U.S. war against the Vietnamese in the 1960s, and suffered the agony of U.S. saturation bombing and the Pol Pot regime in the 1970s.

Contributors include Hou Yuon and Hu Nim, two socialist members of Prince Sihanouk's government in the early 1960s who later went underground to help lead the 1970–75 war against the U.S.-sponsored Lon Nol regime and were themselves murdered in the Pol Pot era. Chanthou Boua, a Kampuchean now living in Australia, suffered the loss of her entire family in the same period.

Kiljunen, Kimmo, ed. ***Kampuchea: Decade of the Genocide. Report of a Finnish Inquiry Commission.*** London: Zed, 1984. 144pp. $9.25. Maps, tables, notes. Available in the United States from the Biblio Distribution Center (Totowa, N.J.).

This short book is a revised and edited version of the Finnish Inquiry Commission's *Kampuchea in the Seventies* published in Helsinki in December 1982. The inquiry commission was established in late 1980 to study—with "strict neutrality" and "with no preconceived goal or ambition"—"the political, social, and economic development of Kampuchea and the subsequent legal implications and repercussions on international politics, especially in light of the events of the 1970's."

The first part of the commission report is a historical survey of the country. The survey begins with the period of colonial and royal rule and then moves forward through Pol Pot's Democratic Kampuchea and on to the establishment of the People's Republic of Kampuchea. The remaining two-thirds of the book covers refugees and opposition movements, the interests of power politics, international humanitarian aid, international law, and the mass media.

Lobe, Thomas. ***United States Security Policy and Aid to the Thailand Police.*** Denver, Colo.: University of Denver, Colorado Seminary, 1977. 161pp. $3.50. Maps, charts, glossary, photographs, notes, appendices.

This is a carefully documented history of U.S. military and police aid to Thailand over a twenty-five year period. It was written by a political scientist who has also researched similar types of U.S. aid to Chile, Bolivia, and Paraguay. *United States Security Policy* provides historical background on U.S. attempts at "social control" in the Third World from the days of John F. Kennedy and then focuses attention on U.S. police aid, the CIA, and the Office of Public Safety (a division of the Agency for International Development) as these all relate to Thailand.

Lobe, author of *United States Police Assistance for the Third World* (University of Michigan, 1975), contends that his case study of Thailand is "more than the history of an agency [the Office of Public Safety]." Rather, he believes, it is "the typical and symbolic history of a policy—the policy of United States intervention and experimentation in social control throughout the Third World over the last two and a half decades. While the specific events have varied, the devastating effects and ends implicit in the policy have come to pass in such diverse places as Bolivia and Laos, Paraguay and Cambodia, and, of course, Vietnam, Chile, and now, Thailand."

Omvedt, Gail. ***We Will Smash This Prison! Indian Women in Struggle.*** London: Zed, 1980. 192pp. $6.95. Glossary, documents, map, bibliographical notes. Available in the United States from the Biblio Distribution Center (Totowa, N.J.).

In *We Will Smash This Prison!* Gail Omvedt offers powerful and discriminating insights into the budding women's movement in India. A skilled researcher and dedicated activist, Omvedt describes events in which she participated during the mid- to late 1970s in the Indian state of Maharashtra.

"In 1975," the author writes, "we set out to organize a women's movement in the conviction that here was a force capable of shaking the foundations of society, an indispensable part of the people's revolutionary movement. For nearly nineteen months I was drawn into this effort, and this book is an attempt to recapture the turmoil and exhilaration of that period. It was written to bring to others something of the reality of Indian women's aspirations and struggles as I experienced them at the time. It was not intended to give a programme for those struggles or an analysis of the Indian women's movement."

Gail Omvedt uses the words of Indian women themselves to tell the stories of the burdens and struggles of rural and urban women workers, and she analyzes the "cultural bondage" of women college students, women in the leftist movements, and the situation of the *adivasis* (tribal people)—"one of the most oppressed sections of India's population." Her narrative culminates in a description of the October 1975 Women's Liberation Struggle Conference.

In her afterword the author states her belief that women of the Third World, doubly downtrodden as they are, must be feminists and socialists.

Permanent Peoples' Tribunal Session on the Philippines. ***Philippines: Repression and Resistance.*** Utrecht, Netherlands: KSP (Komite ng Sambayanang Pilipino), 1981. 298pp. $5.50. Available from the Philippine Resource Center (Berkeley, Calif.).

This powerful indictment of the Marcos dictatorship and its international allies contains the proceedings and judgment of the case brought before the Permanent Peoples' Tribunal in late 1980 by the National Democratic Front (NDF) of the Philippines and the Moro National Liberation Front (MNLF) on behalf of the Filipino people and the Bangsa Moro people respectively.

Contents include: appeals made by the Filipino and Bangsa Moro people, the legal case against the Marcos regime, testimonies about economic, political, and cultural repression and about the resistance movement, and the verdict of the tribunal.

In addition, this publication contains the ten-point program of the NDF, the manifesto of the MNLF, and the reply from President Marcos's office.

Piyadasa, L. ***Sri Lanka: The Holocaust and After.*** London: Marram Books, 1984. 131pp. £4.25. Glossary, illustration, index.

The "holocaust" in the title of this book refers to the racist violence that was unleashed upon the Tamil minority on the island of Sri Lanka (formerly Ceylon) in late July 1983. The author argues passionately that the cause of the savagery of the July pogrom cannot be attributed simply to mob violence by elements of the majority Sinhalese population, but rather is to be located in the very political structure and practices of the ruling Jayawardene government.

Piyadasa frames the dramatic events of July 1983 in a readable description of the island nation and its population of Moors, Malays, Burghers, Sinhalese, and Tamils.

Poole, Fred, and Max Vanzi. ***Revolution in the Philippines: The United States in a Hall of Cracked Mirrors.*** New York: McGraw-Hill, 1984. 357pp. $18.95. Cloth. Map, index.

Novelist Poole and UPI news executive Vanzi team up to present a readable and up-to-the-minute journalistic account of the Philippines from "America's forgotten war" in 1898 through the assassination of Benigno Aquino in August 1983—an event that Vanzi covered. They cover the Moro War in the southern Philippines, the power of the military, the lavish lifestyle of President Marcos and his "cronies," the impact of transnational corporations, and the persecution of Marcos's opponents in the United States.

Selbourne, David. ***Through the Indian Looking-Glass: Selected Articles on India 1976–1980.*** London: Zed, 1982. 239pp. $10.25. Who's Who, notes, appendices. Available in the United States from the Biblio Distribution Center (Totowa, N.J.).

The author, said to be the most widely known foreign commentator on India's increasingly complex and turbulent affairs, writes in his no holds barred style about Indira Gandhi's June 1975 declaration of a state of emergency, the CIA, British "racism and hypocrisy," and the death of "the big white chief across the waters" (Earl Mountbatten, the last viceroy of the British raj). This collection of Selbourne's writings contains, as well, his analysis of the Indian state and political culture, literary writings on Indian daily life, and an obituary of Sanjay Gandhi (Indira's son) that no Indian editor "was prepared to print."

An anthology such as *Through the Indian Looking-Glass* is obviously not designed to present a systematic and complete portrayal of Indian life and politics. It does, however, convey a sharp sense of the ebb and flow of politics on the subcontinent. Selbourne's essays were written in the immediacy of turbulent events with a stubborn refusal to curry favor with any one.

Shalom, Stephen Rosskamm. ***The United States and the Philippines: A Study of Neocolonialism.*** Philadelphia: Institute for the Study of Human Issues, 1981. 302pp. $19.50. Cloth. Maps, tables, notes, bibliography, index.

This well-documented study examines the impact of U.S. policy on the Philippines from the closing days of World War II to around 1980. "My aim in this book," states the author, "is to show that the relationship between the United States and the Philippines since 1946 has been a neocolonial one. I will try to describe how the relationship came about, what the mutual interests of the U.S. and the Philippines elites have been, what mechanisms have served these interests, and what impact neocolonialism has had on the lives of most Filipinos."

In *The United States and the Philippines* Professor Shalom, of William Paterson College in New Jersey, illustrates the many ways in which the Philippines has served as the testing ground for the economic, political, and military instruments of U.S. intervention elsewhere in the Third World.

Shawcross, William. ***Sideshow: Kissinger, Nixon and the Destruction of Cambodia.*** New York: Simon and Schuster, 1979. 464pp. $2.95. Maps, photographs, chronology, notes, bibliography, index.

Sideshow is the best-selling exposé of the U.S. secret and illicit war against Cambodia. The author draws on his experience as a journalist in

Southeast Asia, as well as on interviews and thousands of pages of classified U.S. government documents, to describe how power was employed—and abused—in the U.S. National Security Council, the Pentagon, and the State Department under the leadership of Richard Nixon and his national security assistant, Henry Kissinger.

"This book deals in detail with Cambodia," writes Shawcross, "but I hope it suggests, in a general way, the consequences that other countries face when the world's most powerful nation and, in my opinion, the world's most vital democracy, is governed as it was after Richard Nixon and Henry Kissinger moved into the White House in January 1969."

See also: William Shawcross. *The Quality of Mercy: Cambodia, Holocaust and Modern Conscience.* New York: Simon and Schuster, 1984. 464pp. $19.95. Shawcross scrutinizes the operations of the humanitarian agencies that handled the $1 billion and 500,000 tons of food that were donated worldwide for Cambodia relief in the late 1970s.

Sheridan, Mary, and Janet W. Salaff, eds. ***Lives: Chinese Working Women.*** Bloomington, Ind.: Indiana University Press, 1984. 258pp. $8.95. Notes.

Using the "life history" research method (a blending of history and biography) the writers in this anthology present vivid portrayals of the life and work of women in Hongkong, Taiwan, and the People's Republic of China. As diverse as the portraits are, they share common themes: the responsibilities of eldest daughters, violence in the family, sibling affection and rivalry, and the primacy of men in private affairs. Other lesser themes also surface: moral regulations and personal codes, loyalty, self-interest, sacrifice, and the importance of food and diet.

The editors provide an explanation of the "life history" method, along with an introduction and conclusion.

Siu, Bobby. ***Women of China: Imperialism and Women's Resistance, 1900–1949.*** London: Zed, 1982. 208pp. $8.50. Tables, statistical appendices, notes, bibliography, index. Available in the United States from Biblio Distribution Center (Totowa, N.J.).

Although much has been written on women in China after 1949, Bobby Siu's work is unique in its analysis of the role of Chinese women in resistance and revolution prior to 1949. The author focuses on the first half of the twentieth century for two reasons: (1) because it was during that period that the women's movement emerged and developed as an organized and coordinated historical force, and (2) because that period was such a time of transition for China: from a colonial-feudal-capitalist society to a socialist one.

The author defines her tasks in *Women of China* as showing the links between imperialism and the Chinese women's struggle, giving a systematic account of women's role in social change, and illustrating the interrelationship between repression and struggle. *Women of China* opens with a description of imperialism and its effects on China's economy, then focuses on the impact of imperialism on women and the modes of their resistance. In the final chapter Siu summarizes the lessons she feels should be learned from the Chinese women's movement.

Sobhan, Rehman. ***The Crisis of External Dependence: The Political Economy of Foreign Aid to Bangladesh.*** London: Zed, 1984. 272pp. $10.75. Bibliography, tables, notes, statistical appendices, index. Available in the United States from the Biblio Distribution Center (Totowa, N.J.).

The aim of Professor Sobhan's study is "to analyze the nature, extent, and implications of Bangladesh's dependence on foreign aid to sustain its development process." The pattern of "dependent development" that the author describes "has contributed little to eradicate poverty. Rather," Sobhan contends, "it has accentuated concentrations in the ownership of wealth and inequality in the distribution of income without leading to a significant expansion of the productive forces within the economy."

This well-documented indictment of the perverse impact of foreign aid—written by a former member of the Bangladesh Planning Commission—covers in detail the history of the negotiations over the disbursement of aid, and it surveys Bangladesh's relations with various donor nations and agencies (including the World Bank).

"If Bangladesh is not to remain at the perpetual mercy of the domestic and external political compulsions of the aid donors," Sobhan concludes, "it will have to look within itself to see if there is a more self-reliant path to development." This search for self-reliance is the subject of Sobhan's final chapter.

Appendix 4 is a two-page outline of "some topics for further research on the aid regime in Bangladesh."

Stone, I. F. ***The Hidden History of the Korean War.*** New York: Monthly Review, 1971. 368pp. $6.50. Preface to 2nd edition by Stephen E. Ambrose. Appendices, references, map, index. Published originally in 1952.

Noted columnist I. F. Stone's pathbreaking history of the Korean War was suppressed when it was first written in the early 1950s. The U.S. government and public were not receptive in those days to Stone's piercing questions and firsthand observations about the origins and conduct of the Korean War.

The fact that *Hidden History* is still in print more than thirty years after the events Stone describes is testimony to the integrity of his witness. Recent studies by Bruce Cumings, Gavan McCormick, and others have attested to the accuracy of Stone's early perceptions.

Vickery, Michael. ***Cambodia 1975–1982.*** Boston: South End Press, 1984. 310pp. $9. Maps, notes, bibliography, index.

Why did the Cambodian Revolution take place? Why did it proceed along the lines it did? Why did it fail? And what has been happening since the ousting of the Pol Pot regime in 1979? Michael Vickery brings twenty years of study and experience to his attempts to answer these questions. He speaks all of the Khmer dialects. He has traveled extensively in the country, both before and after Pol Pot's rule, and he has conducted hundreds of personal interviews with refugees—many of whom he had known in the years before they became refugees.

Vickery's forthright and principled analysis of the problems of sources and evidence regarding events in Cambodia is a noteworthy contribution of his work.

Wiseberg, Laurie, and Harry Scoble, eds. ***Access to Justice: The Struggle for Human Rights in South East Asia.*** London: Zed, 1984. 208pp. $10.25. Index. Available in the United States from the Biblio Distribution Center (Totowa, N.J.).

This volume brings together the experiences and ideas of leading human rights campaigners from Indonesia, Thailand, the Philippines, and Malaysia. Lawyers like T. Mulya Lubis and A.B. Nasution, feminists like Sister Mary Soledad Perpignan, and political economists like Randolph David contribute to a broad redefinition of human rights and access to services and to the discussion of the specific needs of particular groups like women and indigenous peoples.

Access to Justice describes the imaginative ways in which people are struggling to assert their human dignity in the face of authoritarian regimes wedded to keeping in power those few Southeast Asians who benefit from U.S. domination of their countries' economies.

Bibliographies

ASIA AND PACIFIC REGION

The ***Journal of Asian Studies*** provides the most comprehensive annual review of literature about the Asia and Pacific region, though the bibliography normally runs four years behind the dates of the published materials. The ***1980 Bibliography of Asian Studies,*** for instance, was published in February/March 1984 (and was announced in the August 1984 edition of the *Journal*). The 1980 edition, edited by Estrella Bryant, listed some fifteen thousand articles and books written in Western languages about Asia and the Pacific. It is available from the Association of Asian Studies, One Lane Hall, University of Michigan, Ann Arbor, MI 48109 for $23.

In the late 1960s and early 1970s the Association of Asian Studies compiled multivolume sets—published in Boston by G. K. Hall—of author and subject bibliographies of Asian studies. The series for 1941-65 appeared in 1970 in four volumes for the author and four volumes for the subject bibliographies. The ***Cumulative Bibliography of Asian Studies, 1966-1970***, publishedin 1972, numbered 3 volumes each for the author and subject bibliographies.

America in Asia: Research Guides on U.S. Economic Activity in Pacific Asia is one of the most comprehensive annotated listings available of primary, Pacific-Asian sources of information on U.S. investments in, trade with, and loans and aid to Hongkong, Indonesia, Japan, South Korea, Malaysia, the Philippines, Singapore, Taiwan, and Thailand. The twenty-one-page chapter on the general Asia area describes organizations and publications in Asia that relate to or cover the entire region. *America in Asia* was published in 1979 by what is now called the Asia Monitor Resource Center (236pp. $10, plus postage).

CHINA

Cheng, Lucie, Charlotte Furth, and Hon-ming Yip, eds. ***Women in China: Bibliography of Available English Language Materials.*** Berkeley, Calif.: University of California, Institute of East Asian Studies, 1984. 109pp. $12. List of sources surveyed, index of Chinese women as subjects, author index.

Women in China contains 4,107 entries, current to the summer of 1981. Materials selected from over 250 journals and almost one hundred bibliographies are classified under twelve general headings and eighty-seven subheadings. General headings are education, emancipation movements, health and population, labor and production, literature, art and folklore, marriage and the family, politics and the law, psychology and religion, science, technology and the military, sport and fashion, and Western women in China. Few of the entries are annotated.

The editors highlight two particularly important categories of published material included in *Women in China.* These are: (1) "imaginative literature," such as novels, poetry, and plays by or about women; and (2) news and opinion articles translated from the post-1950 Chinese press by—among others—the U.S. government-sponsored Joint Publications Research Service.

See also: Karen T. Wei, comp. *Women in China.* Westport, Conn.: Greenwood Press, 1984. 250pp. $35.

Sive, Mary Robinson. ***China: A Multimedia Guide.*** New York: Neal-Schuman, 1982. 245pp. $16.50. Cloth. Appendices, directory of suppliers, title, subject, author and name indexes.

Mary Robinson Sive, editor of *Media Monitor*, a periodical guide to learning resources, and author of *Selecting Instructional Media* and of the "Media Notes" column in *Curriculum Review*, has compiled in *China: A Multimedia Guide* an outstanding source book for anyone involved in teaching or learning about the People's Republic of China.

Sive's book covers materials produced since 1976 for elementary grades, middle school, junior high, and senior high school. The annotated entries (over six hundred of them) are arranged according to grade levels and emphasize materials that break down stereotypical thinking and show respect for cultural differences. They include maps and atlases, professional resources (books, ERIC documents, and organizations useful as continuing sources of information).

A forerunner of this multimedia guide was *China: A Resource and Curriculum Guide,* edited by Arlene Posner and Arne J. deKeijzer. 2nd ed. Chicago: University of Chicago Press, 1976. 317pp. $3.95.

Stanford Program on International and Cross-Cultural Education (SPICE). ***Teaching About China.*** 2 vols. Stanford, Calif.: SPICE, 1983. Vol. 1: ***Cultural Expressions.*** 29pp. $2. Vol. 2: ***People and Daily Life.*** 16pp. $2.

Cultural Expressions is an annotated bibliography of elementary- and secondary-school materials dealing with language, art, thought, literature, music, and theater. The guide also provides information on teaching units developed by various East Asian outreach centers across the United States. (Order stock no. 0315.)

People and Daily Life covers life in the People's Republic of China, in traditional China, and in Chinese American communities. Each item includes units for classroom use, background readings for the teacher, audiovisuals, and supplementary materials. (Order stock no. 0316.)

INDOCHINA

Burns, Richard Dean, and Milton Leitenberg. ***The Wars in Vietnam, Cambodia and Laos, 1945–1982: A Bibliographic Guide.*** War/Peace Bibliography Series No. 18. Santa Barbara, Calif.: ABC-Clio Information Services, 1984. 290pp. Cloth. Chronology, glossary, author index, maps, tables. Also from Clio Press, Oxford, England.

This guide is one in a series of "working bibliographies" being compiled by the Center for the Study of Armament and Disarmament, California State University, Los Angeles, in order "to promote a wider understanding of martial violence and the alternatives to its employment."

The Wars in Vietnam, Cambodia and Laos—an expansion of an earlier (1973) bibliographic guide by the same editors—contains 6,202 individual citations of chronologies, bibliographies, guides and indexes, journals, atlases, articles, books, and other published sources on everything from the domino theory to the punishment of U.S. draft resisters. Citations are not annotated, but the introductory comments and the well-designed organizational format of the book bring the pieces together into a coherent whole.

Olney, Kathryn, and Lee Esbenshade. **"Dealing with Indochina War Issues: A Resource Guide."** In *Southeast Asia Chronicle* 91, October 1983. 5pp. Available from the Asia Resource Center (Washington, D.C.).

This attractive and well-annotated list includes veterans' organizations, resource centers and clearinghouses, newsletters and periodicals, audiovisuals, and books.

Southeast Asia Resource Center. **"The Kampuchea Debate: A Bibliography."** In *Southeast Asia Chronicle* 79, August 1981. 3pp. Available from the Asia Resource Center (Washington, D.C.).

Items in this list include books, magazine articles, and organizations. Some are briefly annotated.

Sugnet, Christopher L., and John T. Hickey. ***Vietnam War Bibliography.*** Lexington, Mass. and Toronto: Lexington Books, D.C. Heath, 1983. 572pp. Appendix, index.

This bibliographical register and its companion 152-page index were born out of the desire of its compilers to improve access to one of the world's largest repositories of literature on U.S. involvement in Vietnam: the John M. Echols Collection in Cornell University's Olin Library. The four thousand items in the bibliographical register are listed alphabetically by title, with data given on the author, publisher, date, number of pages, and library call number. Materials listed are in English, French, and Vietnamese.

NORTH KOREA

Halliday, Jon. **"Further Bibliography on North Korea."** In *Bulletin of Concerned Asian Scholars* 16, no. 4. Fall 1984. 2pp.

This bibliography is a supplement to one that Halliday compiled and published in vol. 11, no. 4 (1979) of the *Bulletin of Concerned Asian Scholars*. The current list was completed on August 31, 1984. Some items are briefly annotated.

SOUTH ASIA

Kozicki, Richard J. ***International Relations of South Asia, 1947–80: A Guide to Information Sources.*** Detroit: Gale Research Company, 1981. 166pp. Volume 10 in Gale's International Relations Information Guide Series. Appendix, indexes.

This bibliography of English-language materials (monographs, articles, and essays) is organized into four major sections: South Asia as a region; India; Pakistan; and Bangladesh, Sri Lanka, Nepal, Bhutan, and Afghanistan. Entries are arranged alphabetically by author and are annotated. The appendix contains a list of 105 "basic books" on the international relations of the countries of South Asia since 1947, as well as on the modern history and domestic politics of these countries. Two indexes (subject and author) make this reference work very easy to use.

Catalogs, Directories, Guides

Heinze, Nancy A., and James T. Magruder, eds. ***Connections: A Resource Guide for Church Leaders.*** New York and Atlanta, Ga.: Presbyterian Church (USA), 1984. 104pp. $2. Title and subject indexes, illustrations.

This guide "to current and major resources that are recommended for use by staff and leaders throughout the Presbyterian Church contains listings of books, audiovisuals, curriculum and worship materials, and other resources on almost one hundred issues, including human rights, economic justice, hunger, and world relief and service. The Asia section contains thirty-six entries.

Ryan, Tim, with Rae Jappinen. ***The Whole Again Resource Guide. An Annual Periodical and Resource Guide.*** Capra Press, P.O. Box 2068, Santa Barbara, CA 93120. 1982. 315pp. $12.95. A 1984 supplement is available from SourceNet, P.O. Box 6767, Santa Barbara, CA 93160. 1984. 250pp. $12.95 (individuals), $19.95 (libraries).

The "peace and social justice" chapter of this resource guide is relevant, though there is only one resource specifically on Asia and the Pacific.

Task Force on Alternatives in Print, Social Responsibilities Round Table, American Library Association. ***Alternatives in Print: An International Catalog of Books, Pamphlets, Periodicals, and Audiovisual Materials.*** 6th ed. New York: Neal-Schuman Publishers, 1980. 668pp. Title, subject, author, and geographical indexes.

This comprehensive guide covers organizations that are alternative in nature—whether they be political, cultural, or literary. Information given includes the name and address of the organization and (unannotated) citations—with author, title, price—of books, periodicals, and audiovisuals published by the organization. Records and tapes are included. *Alternatives in Print* encompasses both U.S. and international organizations.

Wien, Barbara J., ed. ***Peace and World Order Studies: A Curriculum Guide.*** See p. 111 below. The 71-page resource guide in the back of this curriculum guide features funding sources, filmography, periodicals, organizations, and bibliography.

Reference Books

Readers who need detailed background information on the nations and people of Asia and the Pacific should check their libraries for these reference works:

David, Isidoro P., et al., eds. ***Key Indicators of Developing Members of the Asian Development Bank.*** New York: New York University Press, 1985. 368pp. $60. Cloth.

This reference work contains statistical data on twenty-five countries in and bordering on South Asia and Southeast Asia. The data series start in 1970 and present: national accounts by industrial origin and by expenditure; external trade by principal commodities; and external debt and government finance. Sixty-four regional tables allow for easy intercountry comparisons.

The Far East and Australasia. London: Europa Publications, annual.

1984, sixteenth edition. 945pp. $140. Distributed in the United States by Gale Research Company, Book Tower, Detroit, MI 48226.

Major sections: general survey (lengthy articles on population, commodities, religions, etc.), regional organizations (United Nations, Asian Development Bank, and others), and country-by-country surveys. The survey of each country includes information about physical and social geography, history, and economy, and also contains a statistical survey, a directory of organizations, and a bibliography.

Far Eastern Economic Review. ***Asia Yearbook.*** Hongkong: Far Eastern Economic Review, annual.

Since 1960 the editors of the weekly magazine *Far Eastern Economic Review* have compiled a yearbook on the region that includes surveys of critical regional issues, as well as country-by-country presentations with statistical charts and illustrations.

Ghosh, Pradip K., ed. ***Developing South Asia: A Modernization Perspective.*** Westport, Conn., and London: Greenwood Press, 1984. International Development Resource Books, no. 18. Prepared under the auspices of the Center for International Development, University of Maryland, College Park, and the World Academy of Development and Cooperation, Washington, D.C. 582pp. $55. Notes, statistical tables, appendix, bibliography, index.

Though the articles and statistical information in this volume focus on South Asia, the resource bibliography (part 3) and directory of information sources (part 4) contain information on the entire region.

Harvey, Joan M. ***Statistics: Asia and Australasia. Sources for Social, Economic, and Market Research.*** Beckenham, England: CBD Research, 1983. 2nd edition. 440pp. Distributed in the United States by Gale Research Company, Book Tower, Detroit, MI 48226.

This reference work is a well-annotated listing of sources of statistical information in and about Asia and Australasia. These sources include regional and government offices, libraries and information centers, bibliographies of statistics, and major national publications covering statistical information about production, population, social and political trends, and many more categories.

Smith, R. B. ***An International History of the Vietnam War.*** Vol. 1: ***Revolution versus Containment, 1955–61.*** New York: St. Martin's Press, 1984. 301pp. $25. Bibliography, index.

This is the first in a projected four-volume set of reference books on the war in Indochina that is unique in emphasizing international aspects of the conflict, such as Hanoi's relations with China and the Soviet Union throughout the war.

Wasserman, Paul, and Alice E. Kennington. ***Ethnic Information Sources of the United States.*** 2 vols. Detroit: Gale Research, 1983. 1380pp. $135.

Ethnic Information Sources is a guide to organizations, agencies, foundations, institutions, media, commercial and trade bodies, government programs, research institutes, libraries and museums, religious organizations, books, pamphlets, audiovisuals and other resources categorized by ethnic group, such as Brazilians, Koreans, and so forth. The public affairs and cultural and educational categories include some of the institutions listed in the present directory.

SUPPLEMENTARY LIST OF BOOKS

AFGHANISTAN

Democratic Republic of Afghanistan: Background Briefing on Amnesty International's Concerns. London and New York: Amnesty International, October 1983.

BANGLADESH

Hartmann, Betsy, and James Boyce. ***A Quiet Violence: View from a Bangladesh Village.*** London: Zed, 1983.

Lifschultz, Lawrence. ***Bangladesh: The Unfinished Revolution.*** London: Zed, 1979.

BURMA

Khaing, Mi Mi. ***The World of Burmese Women.*** London: Zed, 1984.

CHINA

Ackerman, M. Kahn, ***China Within the Outer Gate,*** Marco Polo Press, 1982.

Chan, Anita, Richard Madsen, and Jonathan Unger. ***Chen Village: The Recent History of a Peasant Community in Mao's China.*** Berkeley and Los Angeles: University of California Press, 1984.

Hinton, William. ***Fanshen: A Documentary of Revolution in a Chinese Village.*** New York: Vintage Books, 1966.

EAST TIMOR

Kohen, Arnold, and John Taylor. ***An Act of Genocide: Indonesia's Invasion of East Timor.*** TAPOL–UK, 1979.

INDIA

Bettelheim, Charles. ***India Independent.*** New York: Monthly Review, 1971.

Bohm, Bob. ***Notes on India.*** Boston: South End Press, 1982.

Davey, Brian. ***The Economic Development of India: A Marxist Analysis.*** London: Spokesman Books, 1975.

Hiro, Dilip. ***Inside India Today.*** New York: Monthly Review, 1979.

Kishwar, Madhu, and Ruth Vanita, eds. ***In Search of Answers: Indian Women's Voices.*** London: Zed, 1984.

INDONESIA

McMahon, Robert J. ***Colonialism and Cold War: The United States and the Struggle for Indonesian Independence, 1945–49.*** Ithaca, N.Y.: Cornell University Press, 1981.

KOREA

Billings, Peggy, et al. ***Fire Beneath the Frost: The Struggles of the Korean People and Church.*** New York: Friendship Press, 1984.

Cumings, Bruce. ***The Origins of the Korean War: Liberation and the Emergence of Separate Regimes, 1945–1947.*** Princeton, N.J.: Princeton University Press, 1981.

McCormack, Gavan. ***Cold War, Hot War: An Australian Perspective on the Korean War.*** Sydney: Hale & Iremonger, 1983.

Selden, Mark, and Gavan McCormack, eds. ***Korea, North and South: The Deepening Crisis.*** New York: Monthly Review, 1980.

Son, Dug-Soo, and Lee Mi-Kyung. ***My Mother's Name Is Worry: A Preliminary Report of the Study on Poor Women in Korea.*** Seoul: Christian Institute for the Study of Justice and Development, 1983.

MALAYSIA

Report of an Amnesty International Mission to the Federation of Malaysia. London and New York: Amnesty International, 1979.

PACIFIC

Howe, K. R. ***Where the Waves Fall: A South Sea Islands History from First Settlement to Colonial Rule.*** Honolulu: University of Hawaii Press, 1985.

Lutz, Catherine, ed. ***Micronesia As Strategic Colony.*** Cambridge, Mass.: Cultural Survival, 1984.

McHenry, Donald. ***Micronesia: Trust Betrayed.*** Washington, D.C.: Carnegie Endowment for International Peace, 1975.

Nevin, David. ***The American Touch in Micronesia: A Story of Power, Money and the Corruption of a Pacific Paradise.*** New York: W.W. Norton, 1974.

PAKISTAN

Hayes, Louis D. ***Politics in Pakistan: The Struggle for Legitimacy.*** Boulder, Colo.: Westview Press, 1984.

Pakistan, Human Rights Violations and the Decline of the Rule of Law. London and New York: Amnesty International, January 1982.

PHILIPPINES

The Philippines: A Country in Crisis. New York: The Lawyers Committee for International Human Rights, December 1983.

The Philippines: Human Rights after Martial Law. Geneva: The International Commission of Jurists, 1984.

Report of an Amnesty International Mission to the Republic of the Philippines, 11–28 November 1981. London and New York: Amnesty International, September 1982.

SINGAPORE

Report of an Amnesty International Mission to Singapore. London and New York: Amnesty International, January 1980.

SRI LANKA

Report of an Amnesty International Mission to Sri Lanka. London and New York: Amnesty International, June 1983.

VIETNAM

Gettleman, Marvin E., Jane Franklin, Marilyn Young, and H. Bruce Franklin. ***Vietnam and America: A Documented History.*** New York: Grove Press, 1985.

Report of an Amnesty International Mission to Vietnam. London and New York: Amnesty International, May 1981.

INFORMATION SOURCES

For lists of other books on the Asia and Pacific region see the bibliographies, catalogs, and reference books described above (pp. 34–40). To keep current on new releases request book catalogs from the publishers represented in this chapter, particularly Monthly Review, Orbis Books, South End Press, Third World Publications, and Zed Press. In addition, the following publications are noteworthy for their coverage of books on countries and issues in the Asia and Pacific region:

China in the Classroom. Resources from the Center for Teaching about China. Washington, D.C.: US-China People's Friendship Association, 1984. 22pp. Free. Illustrations. Available from USCPFA, Center for Teaching about China, 2025 Eye St., NW, Suite 715, Washington, DC 20006.

This attractive guide lists and describes books on China for all levels, preschool on up. Because the USCPFA catalog is such a worthwhile and easily accessible resource, only a few resources on China have been included in the present directory.

Guide to Current Development Literature on Asia and the Pacific. Bangkok: United Nations Asian and Pacific Development Institute, bimonthly. This catalog is published by the Library and Documentation Centre of the Asia Pacific Development Information Service, P.O. Box 2–136, Sri Aydudhya Rd., Bangkok, Thailand.

Social Studies School Service, 1985 Catalog. Culver City, Calif.: Social Studies School Service, 1985. 274pp. Free. Photographs, illustrations. Available from the publisher, 10,000 Culver Blvd., P.O. Box 802, Culver City, CA 90232-0802.

As with the USCPFA catalog described above, the Social Studies School Service's catalog is such an excellent complement to the present directory that it was judged unnecessary to include the many printed and audiovisual resources on Asia and the Pacific found in that catalog. The School Service catalog is free and should be on the bookshelf of all educators concerned with awareness of international affairs.

See also these two publications from Third World Resources:

Third World Resource Directory: A Guide to Organizations and Publications. Edited by Thomas P. Fenton and Mary J. Heffron. Maryknoll, N.Y.: Orbis Books, 1984. 304pp. $17.95, plus $1.50 shipping and handling. Illustrations, indexes. Available from Orbis Books, Maryknoll, NY 10545, or from Third World Resources, 464 19 St., Oakland, CA 94612.

The books section (pp. 17–22) and other resources section (pp. 33–36) of the Third World chapter are noteworthy, as is the entire printed resources section of the chapter on Asia and the Pacific (pp. 68–71). Cross-references in those sections direct readers to entries in other chapters (e.g., on women or human rights) that are related to Asia and the Pacific.

Third World Resources: A Quarterly Review of Resources from and about the Third World. 4 issues/year. Newsletter. 28cm. 16pp. $25/year (organizational subscription), $25/two years (individual subscription). Inquire for overseas rates. Subscriptions are available on a calendar-year basis only. Write: Third World Resources, 464 19 St., Oakland, CA 94612.

3

Periodicals

This chapter is divided into three parts: annotated entries, supplementary list of periodicals, and sources of additional information on periodicals related to Asia and the Pacific.

Each **annotated entry** includes: title; address; frequency of publication; format (magazine, newsletter, newspaper); size (height in centimeters and number of pages); subscription costs; keyword description of format; and description of content.

Quotation marks in the annotations enclose the words of the periodical's publisher, editor, or promotional materials.

Periodicals in the **supplementary list** (pp. 55–58) are grouped under these headings: general Asia and Pacific-oriented (subdivided by type: academic, church-related or focused, and news-oriented); China (subdivided into academic, church-related, and popular types); East Timor; Indonesia; Korea; Pacific; Philippines; and Thailand. Entries in this section include title; address; frequency of publication; and type of periodical.

The **information sources** section (pp. 58–59) provides an annotated list of directories and guides that contain the names of other periodicals related to Asia and the Pacific.

All periodical titles and related organizations in this chapter are listed in the appropriate indexes at the back of this directory. Check through the organizations chapter above for the names of additional periodicals.

ANNOTATED ENTRIES

AMPO: Japan-Asia Quarterly Review, PARC: Pacific-Asia Resource Center, C.P.O. Box 5250, Tokyo International, Tokyo, Japan. 4 issues/year. Magazine. 24cm. 100pp. Individual subscription: $16/year. Institutional subscription: $24/year. Inquire for overseas airmail rates. Back issues available, $4/each. Feature articles, New Asia News, photographs, illustrations, notes, advertisements.

AMPO has its origins in late 1969 with the Japanese "Peace for Vietnam Committee" and an affiliated organization of foreign residents in Japan. The magazine focused considerable energies at the start on opposition to the 1970 Japan-U.S. Security Treaty. (*AMPO* is an abbreviated form of Japan-U.S. Security Treaty.) The review is "designed to overcome the fact that the Japanese left, one of the most articulate and active movements in the world, is covered by a blanket of silence in all languages but Japanese."

AMPO presents well-documented radical analyses of political, economic, and military issues in Asia in a jargon-free style. Typical articles are about workers and labor unions in Thailand, challenges to French nuclear colonialism in the South Pacific, human rights in Korea, and the International Monetary Fund in the Philippines. Literature, drama, and art are also covered.

From time to time *AMPO* devotes an entire issue to one theme. Vol. 8, no. 4 (1977), for instance, was a major 212-page study of free trade zones and the industrialization of Asia.

Ang Katipunan, Union of Democratic Filipinos (KDP), P.O. Box 2759, Oakland, CA 94602. 11 issues/year. Newspaper. 45cm. 16pp. Individual subscription: $10/year. Institutional subscription: $12/year. Back issues available, $1.50/each. Feature articles, editorials, columns, interviews, essays, book reviews, poems, short stories, photographs, illustrations.

This national newsmagazine of the Union of Democratic Filipinos (KDP) bills itself as "a socialist periodical for the Filipino community." The paper is hard-hitting in its criticisms of the Marcos regime and of Washington's support for political repression and economic oppression in the Philippines.

Consistent with KDP's political aims, *Ang Katipunan* also presents analyses of issues that directly affect the Filipino community in North America, as well as of other international foreign policy news. Thus, the newspaper offers news and commentary about such topics as events in Kampuchea, the murder of a California State University professor sympathetic to Vietnam, bilingual education, and the elections in Nicaragua.

Asia Labour Monitor, Asia Monitor Resource Center (AMRC), 444–46 Nathan Rd., 8-B, Kowloon, Hongkong. 6 issues/year. Magazine. 28cm. 36 pp. Individual subscription: $15/year. Institutional subscription: $40/year. Airmail postage extra. Back issues available. Digest of news reports; contains feature articles, charts, tables, book reviews, subject and country indexes, photographs, illustrations.

The *Monitor* is a bimonthly compilation and digest of news gathered from Asian and international newspapers and magazines about labor events and conditions in Asia. Its aim is "to provide clear, concise facts to unions, labour groups and labour activists" with the hope that this information "will be found useful by all who are working on the struggle to improve the livelihoods and rights of the working people of Asia."

Information is organized according to trades or, when it is not about a specific trade, according to country. The trade section includes information about agricultural and plantation workers, electronics and electrical goods workers, public service workers, textile and garment workers, and more. The center believes that organizing labor information "on a trade basis should assist such groups to compare conditions in neighbouring countries." Thus, for instance, there are reports of fatal accidents in mines in Malaysia and Taiwan along with news of a strike by mine workers in the Philippines.

News of general economic activity in Asia is also provided in an effort to "help labour organizations with the important task of planning their activities with an understanding of world economic trends and forces."

A further stated aim of the *Asia Labour Monitor* is to "assist labour unions and groups in the industrialized countries outside Asia to better understand and support workers in developing Asia, for the benefit of both."

As was the case with its predecessor, *Asia Monitor*, the magazine serves as an index to the voluminous periodical clipping files of the Asia Monitor Resource Center. Use of the code number that accompanies each item in the *Monitor* enables AMRC staff to retrieve the original articles that were used in producing the digest.

Asia Link, Center for the Progress of Peoples (CPP), 48 Princess Margaret Rd., 1st floor, Kowloon, Hongkong. 6 issues/year. Newsletter. 30cm. 28pp. Individual subscription: $13/year. Institutional subscription: $13/year. $8.50/year within Asia. Both 2nd class airmail. Incorporates ***Network: A Publication of Hot-Line Asia-Oceania*** and ***Labor Communications***, both of which are available separately. Feature articles, news digests, commentaries, interviews, book reviews, photographs, illustrations.

This house organ of the Center for the Progress of Peoples presents news and commentary on the church and its activities in support of the poor and oppressed in Asia. Feature articles in the past have treated topics such as the Christian contribution to people's participation in social transformation in Asia; Islam, statehood, and human rights; and Vatican criticisms of liberation theology.

Network, a project of the Justice and Peace Coordinating Committee for Asia and Oceania, administered by CPP, is a digest of human rights news from throughout the Asia region. *Labor Communications* uses a similar format to cover labor news in the region.

Asian Action, Asian Cultural Forum on Development (ACFOD), P.O. Box 2930, Bangkok, Thailand. 6 issues/year. Magazine. 28cm. 20pp. Individual subscription: $15/year. Institutional subscription: $15/year. Individuals in developing countries, $9/year. Feature articles, illustrations.

Since 1976 this publication of the Asian Cultural Forum on Development has sought "to provide improved communication between rural development workers in Asia and those, both inside and outside the region, who are interested in development work."

Asian Action is a compilation of information provided by the agencies and individuals associated with ACFOD. This information covers ongoing field and research programs in Malaysia, Thailand, India, the Philippines,

Bangladesh, Sri Lanka, Nepal, Japan, Australia, and New Zealand and is published in order "to share field experiences, convey information about new skills and approaches to development problems, and evaluate projects and elaborate feedback techniques."

Asian Bureau Australia Newsletter, Asian Bureau Australia, 173 Royal Parade, Parkville, Victoria 3052, Australia. 4 issues/year. Newspaper. 40cm. 8pp. Individual subscription: $10/year. Institutional subscription: $10/year (Australian dollars). News reports, feature articles, reports on the Asian Bureau Australia, book reviews, poetry, illustrations, photographs.

This tabloid aims "to make Australians more aware of the developing social, economic, and religious life in Asia and the Western Pacific." In addition, it keeps friends and supporters of the Asian Bureau Australia informed about the organization's activities in the region.

Asian Rights Advocate, Church Committee for Human Rights in Asia, 5253 N. Kenmore, Chicago, IL 60640. 12 issues/year. Newsletter. 28cm. 4pp. Individual subscription: $5/year. Institutional subscription: $5/year. Overseas: $10/year. Human rights-related news items, action suggestions, resources, illustrations.

Published monthly since 1978, the *Advocate* "reviews current events and human stories of the struggles for human rights in Korea, Taiwan, and the Philippines" and "calls for concerted actions by U.S. citizens in solidarity with the people in the movements for justice in those countries."

News items are presented in brief and popular style and are well-complemented by recommendations for action and listings of resources for further study.

BALAI Asian Journal, BALAI Fellowship, P.O. Box SM-366, Manila, Philippines. 4 issues/year. Magazine. 30cm. 26pp. Individual subscription: $12/year. Institutional subscription: $25/year. Inquire for other rates. Back issues available, $2.50/each. Feature articles, notes, news reports, resources, letters to the editor, statistical tables and figures, photographs, illustrations.

This attractive quarterly set out in 1980 to profile the riches of the Third World and of Asia and the Pacific in particular. "Somehow," the editors write, "the viewpoint so far in discovering Asia has been: 'What can Western technology exploit in Asia's resources?' " BALAI determined to expose what Western technology—in the hands of transnational corporations—was doing to the tremendous natural and human resources of the region.

Each issue of the magazine has been devoted to one theme, some of these being: forest destruction in Asia, marine wealth, women in Asia, land use in the region, strategic minerals, and food production and distribution in Asia.

Articles are attractively presented and combine radical analyses with a popular writing style.

Bulletin of Concerned Asian Scholars, P.O. Box R, Berthoud, CO 80513. 4 issues/year. Magazine. 28cm. 72pp. Individual subscription: $20/

year. Institutional subscription: $40/year. List of back issues available. Inquire about other rates. Feature articles, review articles, notes, bibliographies, photographs, illustrations, resources, list of books received.

Since 1968 this academic journal has published lengthy, well-documented articles written from a progressive political point of view on issues related to imperialism, revolution, and social change in Asia. The articles have focused on topics such as capitalist agriculture and rural classes in India; economic reform in China after Mao; state and industrial labor in South Korea; the political economy of agricultural reforms in Vietnam; and worker health and Japanese management in Singapore. The *Bulletin* also treats literary themes and has, in the past, devoted entire issues to anthologizing Asian literature.

The *Bulletin* advertises itself as "independent, progressive and critical; illustrated and literate, without jargon; international in editors, authors, and readers; and preferred by specialists and scholars."

Canada Asia Currents, Canada Asia Working Group, 11 Madison Ave., Toronto, Ontario M5R 2S2, Canada. 4 issues/year. Magazine. 28cm. 16pp. Individual subscription: $6/year. Institutional subscription: $10/year. Back issues available, $1.50/each. News articles, photographs, illustrations.

Canada Asia Currents reports on human rights-related stories in Asia, especially those that have some connection to Canadian political and economic involvement in the region. Many of the news stories are directly relevant to the church—appeals to Canadian churches to aid in the reconstruction of Vietnam and stories of patriotic Catholics participating in the rebuilding of Vietnam.

East Timor Update, East Timor Human Rights Committee, P.O. Box 363, Clinton Station, Syracuse, NY 13201. 4 issues/year. Newsletter. 28cm. 8pp. Individual subscription: $5/year. Institutional subscription: $10/year. Back issues available, $2/each. Inquire for other rates. News reports, updates on United Nations and congressional activity related to East Timor, book reviews, list of news articles, resources, action suggestions, photographs, illustrations.

Since the summer of 1981 this modest newsletter has served to keep concerned North Americans abreast of developments in East Timor's struggle for self-determination. It has carried reports on the church in East Timor, the Fretilin resistance organization, the role of Catholic Relief Services in East Timor, and visits to the United States by Indonesian officals.

Focus on Asian Studies, Asia Society, P.O. Box 1308-M, Fort Lee, NJ 07024. 3 issues/year. Magazine. 28cm. 64pp. Individual subscription: $5/year. Institutional subscription: $16/year. Feature articles, columns, editorial, book reviews, interviews, calendar of events, letters to the editor, curriculum suggestions, photographs, art, illustrations.

This highly polished periodical is published in cooperation with two standing committees of the Association of Asian Studies—the Committee on Teaching about Asia and the Asianists' Teaching Network. *Focus on Asian Studies* is designed "to bring educators both general and specific information on Asia that might otherwise escape their attention. These include curriculum materials and resources that can be used by area specialists, non-specialists, and educators at all levels of education."

Each issue is devoted to one theme, such as Asian geography, the people of Asia, or Asian languages. Articles are richly illustrated. The resource guides and reviews of books and curriculum materials are ample and well-annotated.

Educators will find *Focus on Asian Studies* to be a welcome and most useful tool in opening the eyes of their students to this marvelous region of the world. Readers of *Focus* should be aware, however, that they are seeing Asia from only one point of view. For, as often happens with glossy publications from highly respected institutions such as the Asia Society, the turbulence of Third World peoples' struggles for liberation is severely downplayed—when mentioned at all—in *Focus*.

Global Electronics Information Newsletter, Pacific Studies Center, 222B View St., Mountain View, CA 94041. 12 issues/year. Newsletter. 28cm. 4pp. Individual subscription: $5/year. Institutional subscription: $5/year. Airmail postage extra. Back issues available, 50 cents/each. News digest; also contains notices of resources, statistical tables, illustrations.

This brief newsletter provides a steady summary of reports about the global electronics industry. The reports are synthesized from periodicals such as the *San Jose Mercury News, Aviation Week and Space Technology, Info World,* and the *Wall Street Journal* and cover issues such as runaway shops, toxic hazards in production of electronic components, labor actions, and industrial pollution. Much of the material in the newsletter is Asia-related.

IBON: Facts & Figures, IBON Databank Philippines, 4427 Int. Old Sta. Mesa, P.O. Box SM-447, Manila, Philippines. 26 issues/year. Newsletter. 28cm. 8–12pp. Individual subscription: $15/year. Institutional subscription: $30/year. Back issues are available in bound annual editions. Available in North America from Synapses, 1821 W. Cullerton, Chicago, IL 60608. Feature articles, economic news reports, notes, statistical figures and tables, photographs, illustrations.

This newsletter is about the nuts and bolts of economic life in the Philippines—simply explained and graphically illustrated. The editors of *IBON* are skilled at translating the arcane verbiage of economists into facts and figures that laypeople can grasp—and, more importantly, use to the benefit of working people throughout the Philippines. Whether it is plant shutdowns or nontraditional exports or surveys of the sugar and coconut industries or the economics of national elections—*IBON*'s writers bring the issues home to Filipino readers much as they did with their analysis of why *pan de sal* (the breakfast bread consumed in over 80 percent of the country's households) is literally shrinking in size as the price of wheat flour increases from year to year.

IBON is admirable not just for the economic insights it uniquely provides but also because it is a model of clear and persuasive writing about economic and political affairs.

Indochina Issues, Center for International Policy, Indochina Project, 236 Massachusetts Ave., NE, Suite 505, Washington, DC 20002. 10 issues/year. Magazine. 28cm. 8pp. Individual subscription: $9/year. Institutional subscription: $9/year. Overseas airmail, $19. Back issues available, $1/each. Feature article, illustrations.

In keeping with the aims of its sponsoring organization, the Center for International Policy, this publication seeks "to develop a better understanding of the countries of Indochina and their relations with the United States." Each edition of *Indochina Issues* contains a feature-length analysis, written by a recognized Indochina specialist, of one aspect of the economy, politics, military, or social life of Vietnam, Kampuchea, and Laos.

The newsletter is well-designed and the text well-edited. Numerous back issues of the newsletter are listed in the Pamphlets and Articles section of this directory. *Indochina Issues* is very useful for classroom or group study about Indochina.

Indonesia Reports, Indonesia Publications, P.O. Box 895, N. College Park Sta., College Park, MD 20740. 12 issues/year. 28cm. 57pp. plus supplements. Individual subscription: $49/year. Institutional subscription: $49/year. Apply for other rates. Feature articles, news reports, bibliographies, book and dissertation reviews, documents.

Indonesia Reports details virtually everything about day-to-day political, economic, and social life in Indonesia. Launched in the fall of 1984, this monthly publication consists of single-spaced, typed news items, commentary, documentation, and reviews. It also contains a unique log that summarizes major reports found in Indonesian-language newspapers and other public sources.

Every month Indonesia Publications also makes available five supplements, each of which focuses on one of the following topics: politics, human rights, culture, books and bibliographies, and business. The latter two are available separately ($33/year and $67/year respectively); the other supplements are available only to *Indonesia Reports* subscribers.

Solidarity organizations will find the monthly human rights supplement particularly useful. The March 20, 1985, issue, for instance, carried four documents relating to events inside Irian Jaya and to the Irian-Papua New Guinea border situation.

Inside Asia. 242-44 Pentonville Rd., London N1 9UP, England. 6 issues/year. Magazine. 27cm. 54pp. Individual subscription: £15/year. Institutional subscription: £20/year. Back issues available, £1.50 or $2.75 per issue. Feature articles, editorial, comment and analysis, notes, resources, literature, book reviews, advertising, photographs, illustrations.

Launched in late 1984 this attractive newsmagazine has quickly established itself as an outstanding source of progressive political coverage of Asian affairs.

The editors intend *Inside Asia* to be "popular" in style and "campaigning" in political purpose. In the wake of the Vietnam War, the massacre of the left in Indonesia, the escalation of conflicts on the Indian subcontinent, and the armed engagements between socialist countries in Southeast Asia, the editors state their desire to provide a forum for "the widest possible range of well-argued viewpoints from a radical perspective," especially for "those groups and viewpoints on Asia that are not able to find ready expression in the limited existing channels."

The magazine regularly features a "focus" section on a subject such as aid to Bangladesh, along with its standard coverage of labor affairs, human rights, women in Asia, environment, economy and development, and more. *Inside Asia* is noteworthy for its treatment of regions and issues that receive little attention in the establishment press in North America: the struggle for independence in West Papua (Irian Jaya), working conditions in Malaysia's electronics and rubber industries, the trade union movement in Indonesia, and China's developing nuclear capabilities, among others.

The magazine is always as advertised: "lively, well-written, diverse in its interests, and analytic in its treatment of issues."

Journal of Contemporary Asia, P.O. Box 49010, Stockholm 49, Sweden. 4 issues/year. Magazine. 21cm. 90pp. Individual subscription: $18/year. Institutional subscription: $18/year. Feature articles, book reviews, documents, advertisements.

This journal usually contains four or five feature articles examining such topics as how the foreign policy of the United States, agrarian reform, development strategies, and growth and planning theory relate to the Asian region. The approach is scholarly; the political point of view is progressive. Book reviews are lengthy.

Kasarinlan, Third World Studies Center, P.O. Box 210, University of the Philippines, Diliman, Quezon City, Philippines. 4 issues/year. Magazine. 22cm. 30pp. Individual subscription: $20/year. Institutional subscription: $30/year. Feature articles, reviews, documents, commentaries, source materials.

This quarterly journal of the Third World Studies Center presents analyses of "issues confronting the political, economic, and social lives of peoples in the Third World, particularly in the Philippines and Asia." The first issue (June 1985) contained the following feature articles: "Imperialism, Militarization, and Human Rights in Asia" by Randolf David, "Filipino Labor Outmigration: A Preliminary Analysis" by Arnel de Guzman, "U.S. Intervention in Nicaragua" by Edmundo Garcia, and "The Culture of Resistance: A Study of Protest Songs from 1972–1980" by Teresita Gimenez-Maceda. Also included are commentaries on the Philippine political crisis and the controversial Philippine nuclear power plant, reviews of contemporary Filipiniana, and documents and source materials.

Korea Communiqué, Emergency Christian Conference on Korean Problems, c/o NCC-Japan, No. 24, 2–3–18 Nishi Waseda, Shinjuku-ku, Tokyo 160, Japan. 4 issues/year. Magazine. 28cm. 40pp. Individual subscription: $15/year. Institutional subscription: $15/year. Airmail postage included. Editorial, news reports, documentation, analyses, illustrations, photographs, resources.

Korea Communiqué is the most up-to-date and comprehensive English-language source for human rights news from Korea. The magazine covers U.S. foreign policy relating to South Korea, the student and labor movements, social justice activities of the churches, and political prisoners. Reproductions of articles from English-language newspapers or from Amnesty International reports are often included.

Korea Pamphlet Series, Committee for a New Korea Policy, 221 Central Ave., Albany, NY 12206. 4 issues/year. Newsletter. 22cm. 6pp. Individual subscription: $10/year. Institutional subscription: $15/year. Bulkrates, $5.50/100, plus postage. Topical analysis, illustrations, notes, resources.

The Committee for a New Korea Policy issues these leaflets on a regular basis to promote study and action about one particular aspect of Korean affairs. The text is succinct and nonrhetorical. At the same time the authors do not shy away from tackling sensitive political issues such as the role of U.S. banks in South Korea, formal talks between the United States and North Korea, and the relationship between prostitution and U.S. armed forces in Korea.

Titles in the series include: "Patterns of U.S. Intervention: Eight Parallels in South Korea, El Salvador, The Philippines"; "Should U.S. Policy toward Korea Be Changed?"; "South Korea and the Philippines: Common Problems, Common Struggles"; "Women Fight Back: Women Workers in South Korea"; and "Americans and Third World Workers: Friends or Foes?"

Korea/Update, North American Coalition for Human Rights in Korea, 110 Maryland Ave., NE, Washington, DC 20002. 12 issues/year. Newsletter. 28cm. 24pp. Individual subscription: $15/year. Institutional subscription: $15/year. Includes *Korea/Action* and *Korea Communiqué.* News reports, commentary, action suggestions, resources, network news, "voices from Korea," photographs, illustrations.

Korea/Update includes reports on the human rights situation in Korea written from the perspective of the progressive church. Articles have covered press censorship, Washington's ties with South Korean President

Chun, the operations of U.S. transnational corporations, the massacre in Kwangju, and U.S. armed forces in Korea.

Pacific Bulletin, Pacific Concerns Resource Center (PCRC), P.O. Box 27692, Honolulu, HI 96827. 6 issues/year. Newsletter. 28cm. 8pp. Individual subscription: $10/year. Institutional subscription: $10/year. Back issues available, $1/each. News reports, commentary, action suggestions, resources, network news, illustrations, calendar.

This newsletter is issued bimonthly by the Pacific Concerns Resource Center "in support of the Nuclear Free and Independent Pacific Movement." Vol. 1, no. 1 appeared in March 1981.

News reports in the *Bulletin* cover the struggles for independence in French-governed New Caledonia and in East Timor, the dumping of nuclear wastes in the Pacific, the situation of indigenous peoples in Australia and Aotearoa (New Zealand), the deployment of U.S. nuclear weapons in the Pacific, and more.

The PCRC's unique literature distribution service carries over five hundred pamphlets and articles about issues related to the Pacific. Each issue of the *Bulletin* updates the resource list with titles of new acquisitions.

Pandanus Periodical, Pacific Concerns Resource Center, P.O. Box 27692, Honolulu, HI 96827. 6 issues/year. Newsletter. 28cm. 4pp. Individual subscription: $10/year. Institutional subscription: $10/year. Back issues available, $1.50/each. Feature article, resources, illustrations.

The editors named this newsletter after the Pandanus fruit plant—one that has many uses (including food, building material, and handicrafts)—to symbolize the self-reliance of the people of the Pacific. *Pandanus Periodical*, say the editors, "will provide news and views on economic, energy, environmental, and political ideas and on alternatives that are being used in different islands of the Pacific."

Philippine Research Bulletin, Philippine Information and Research Center, c/o Friends of the Filipino People, P.O. Box 2125, Durham, NC 27702. 4 issues/year. Newsletter. 28cm. 8pp. Individual subscription: $5/year. Institutional subscription: $10/year. Feature article, notes, illustrations.

In the first issue of this newsletter, which appeared in summer 1984, the editors defined the aims of the *Philippine Research Bulletin*: "(1) to serve as a forum for an exchange of views, discussion, and debate on Philippine politics, economics, and society; (2) to fulfill a perceived need for a multidisciplinary, research-oriented publication that would be equally accessible to an academic and non-academic audience; (3) to be both informative and analytical; (4) to present findings as well as to offer interpretations of those findings."

The editors share a concern "that the American public remains largely uninformed about the politics, economics, history, and culture of a country that is considered to be of strategic importance to the United States." "It is our belief," they continue, "that relatively few Americans are aware of the extensive links of their government with that of the Philippines and of the dominant role the United States has played in Philippine political, economic, and cultural life since the turn of the century."

The objective of the *Bulletin*, the editors conclude, "is to achieve a deeper comprehension of the changing Philippine political, economic, and social realities."

The first issue of the *Philippine Research Bulletin* featured a lengthy article by the editors, Gerald Sussman, David O'Connor, and Charles Lindsey: "Philippines, 1984: The Political Economy of a Dying Dictatorship."

Friends of the Filipino People (FFP) also publishes *FFP Bulletin* and *FFP Update* for members of the nationwide organization.

Solidaridad II, Resource Center for Philippine Concerns, C.P.O. Box 1110, Tokyo 100–91, Japan. 4 issues/year. Magazine. 28cm. 36pp. Individual subscription: $25/year. Institutional subscription: $35/year. Back issues available, $1/each. Feature articles, news reports, network news, letters to the editor, commentary, resources, book and film reviews, photographs, illustrations.

Launched in 1977 *Solidaridad II* has grown to become the premier international magazine for news and progressive commentary on the Philippines. Major sections in the magazine are: Update (short news updates), Situationer (column-length news reports), Philippines (lengthy news articles), Monitor (news of Philippine personalities), Solidarity Front (reports on Philippines-related solidarity activities from around the world), Overseas Section (for example, an article on military links between Australia and the Philippines), Perspective (commentary), and Alternative Resources.

Synapses Messages, Synapses, 1821 W. Cullerton, Chicago, IL 60608. 6 issues/year. Newsletter. 22cm. 12pp. Individual subscription: $5/year. Institutional subscription: $5/year. Suggested donation. News reports, action suggestions, network news, letters to the editor, resources, illustrations.

"A synapse," the editors explain, "is the tiny space between two nerve endings in the body. Unless messages are sent across this space, life is not possible. . . . Transposed to the global body, Synapses is a flow of ideas, energy, sharing across the continents. The purpose of *Synapses Messages* is to link issues of justice domestically and internationally."

Taiwan Communiqué, International Committee for Human Rights in Taiwan (ICHRT), P.O. Box 45205, Seattle, WA 98105. 5 issues/year. Magazine. 22cm. 24pp. Individual subscription: $10/year. Institutional subscription: $10/year. First class and airmail postage extra. Feature articles, news reports, commentary, reprints of published news articles, charts, statistical figures and tables, photographs, illustrations.

Taiwan Communiqué furthers the aims of the ICHRT: "the release of political prisoners in Taiwan" and support for "the establishment of a free and democratic political system on the island."

Articles analyze and report on the Sino-British accord on the future of Hongkong, press censorship in Taiwan, political activities of Taiwanese opposition leaders, political prisoners, congressional hearings related to Taiwan, and restrictions placed on religious organizations in Taiwan.

TAPOL Bulletin, British Campaign for the Defence of Political Prisoners and Human Rights in Indonesia, 8a Treport St., London SW18 2BP, England. 6 issues/year. Newsletter. 30cm. 20pp. Individual subscription: £10/year. Institutional subscription: £14/year. Overseas airmail. Back issues available, £2.50/each, plus postage. Feature articles, news reports, documents, book reviews, photographs, illustrations.

The story of human rights violations in Indonesia is—unfortunately—a well-kept secret. One would search in vain, for example, to find a report in the mainstream press of the May 1985 execution of Indonesian trade union leader Mohammed Munir. Munir's secret and summary execution (the government refused to delay the execution to allow Munir a final meeting with his wife) came thirteen years after the government sentenced him to death and eighteen years after his arrest in the wake of the military takeover in the mid-1960s. The British Campaign's bimonthly bulletin, *TAPOL*, carried the story of this first state execution in fifteen years of a political prisoner convicted in connection with the events of October 1965.

Munir's story is just one among the many stories of human rights violations that *TAPOL* chronicles in each issue. Reports in the bulletin are well-documented and professionally prepared.

US-China Review, US-China People's Friendship Association (USCPFA), 2025 Eye St., NW, Suite 715, Washington, DC 20006. 6 issues/year. Magazine. 28cm. 32pp. Individual subscription: $12/year. Institutional subscription: $14/year. Back issues available, $2/each. Inquire for other rates. Feature articles, news reports, letters to the editor, book reviews, poetry, literature, network news, resources, photographs, illustrations, advertisements.

This attractively illustrated magazine contains popularly written articles on all aspects of life in China from the stone sculpture of Dazu in northern China to the writings of Lu Xun. In addition, there are reports on activities of the USCPFA and substantial book reviews.

U.S. Pacific Issues Network Newsletter, U.S. Pacific Issues Network, 1203 Smith Tower, Seattle, WA 98104. 4 issues/year. Newsletter. 28cm. 12pp. Individual subscription: $10/year. Institutional subscription: $10/year. Cost with periodic action alerts, $12/year. News reports, commentary, reprints of published news articles, action suggestions, resources, illustrations, photographs.

The purpose of this newsletter is to keep members of the network informed of developments in the Pacific related to U.S. nuclear weapons testing and deployment, the U.S. compact with the Marshall Islands, ocean dumping of nuclear wastes, and other issues that are of concern to the U.S. Pacific Issues Network.

SUPPLEMENTARY LIST OF PERIODICALS

GENERAL ASIA AND PACIFIC

Academic

Asian Survey, University of California Press, 2120 Berkeley Way, Berkeley, CA 94720. Monthly journal.

Journal of Asian Studies, Association of Asian Studies, One Lane Hall, University of Michigan, Ann Arbor, MI 48109. Quarterly journal.

South Asia Bulletin, Asian American Studies Center, University of California at Los Angeles, Los Angeles, CA 90024. Semiannual journal.

Church-related or Focused

Asia Focus, Union of Catholic Asian News (UCAN), P.O. Box 69626, Kwuntong, Hongkong. Weekly newsletter.

Asia Partnership for Human Development Newsletter, Asia Partnership for Human Development, 154 Elizabeth St., 4th floor, Sydney, New South Wales 2000, Australia. Bimonthly newsletter.

Asian Women Workers Newsletter, Christian Conference of Asia—Urban Rural Mission, 57 Peking Rd., 5th floor, Kowloon, Hongkong. Occasional newsletter.

CCRAI Documentation Series, Center for Christian Response to Asian Issues (CCRAI), c/o Asian Documentation Program of the National Christian Council of Japan, 2-3-18 Nishi-Waseda, Rm. 57, Shinjuku-ku, Tokyo 160, Japan. Quarterly magazine.

CCTD Newsletter, Catholic Council of Thailand for Development, 2508–2510 Soi Saensuk, Prachasingkroh Rd., Bangkok 10400, Thailand. Bimonthly commentary.

Impact: Asian Magazine for Human Transformation, 2948 Noel St., United Paranaque III, Paranaque, Metro Manila, Philippines. Bimonthly magazine.

News-oriented

AfricAsia, Société d'Editions Afrique Asie Amerique Latine, 13 rue d'Uzes, Paris, France. Monthly magazine; progressive political perspective.

Asiaweek, 22 Westlands Rd., Quarry Bay, Hongkong. Weekly magazine.

Far Eastern Economic Review, Centre Point, 181–185 Gloucester Rd., Hongkong. Weekly magazine.

South, 80 Haymarket, New Zealand House, 13th floor, London SW1Y 4TS, England. Monthly with Third World perspective.

CHINA

See the US-China Peoples Friendship Association's ***China in the Classroom: Resources from the Center for Teaching about China*** (p. 42 above) for information on periodicals from China.

Academic

Australian Journal of Chinese Affairs, Contemporary China Centre, Australian National University, P.O. Box 4, Canberra, ACT 2601, Australia. Semiannual journal.

China Quarterly, School of Oriental and African Studies, Malet St., London WC1E 7HP, England. Quarterly journal.

Modern China, Sage Publications, P.O. Box 5024, Beverly Hills, CA 90210. Quarterly journal.

Church-Related

China Notes, National Council of Churches (USA), China Program, 475 Riverside Dr., Rm. 616, New York, NY 10115. Bimonthly newsletter.

China Talk, United Methodist Church, Board of Global Ministries, 2 Man Wan Rd., 17-C, Kowloon, Hongkong. Bimonthly newsletter.

Popular

China Now, Society for Anglo-Chinese Understanding, 152 Camden High St., London NW1 ONE, England. Bimonthly magazine; progressive political viewpoint.

EAST TIMOR

East Timor News, P.O. Box A716, Sydney, NSW 2000, Australia.

Timor Information Service, P.O. Box 77, Clifton Hill, Victoria 3068, Australia.

Timor Newsletter, Rua Damasceno 14a–R/c, 1100 Lisbon, Portugal.

See also: periodicals on Indonesia such as ***Indonesia Reports*** (p. 50 above), ***TAPOL Bulletin*** (p. 54 above), and ***Inside Indonesia*** (below).

INDONESIA

Human Rights Forum, Legal Aid Institute of Indonesia (YLBHI), Jalan Diponegoro 74, Jakarta 10320, Indonesia.

Inside Indonesia, Indonesia Resources and Information Programme (IRIP), P.O. Box 190, Northcote, Victoria 3070, Australia. Quarterly magazine; progressive political point of view.

KOREA

Korea Report, American Friends Service Committee, Korea Program, 1501 Cherry St., Philadelphia, PA 19102. Occasional newsletter.

Korea Scope, International Christian Network for Democracy in Korea, P.O. Box 904, New York, NY 10027. Quarterly magazine; Christian perspective.

Monthly Review of Korean Affairs, P.O. Box 3657, Arlington, VA 22203. Monthly academic journal.

MALAYSIA

Asian Workers Solidarity Link: Malaysia, c/o Sahabat Alam Malaysia, 37 Birch Lane, Penang, Malaysia.

PACIFIC

The Indian Ocean Newsletter, c/o Indian Ocean Information and Documentation Bank (BIDOI), 39 rue du Sentier, 75002 Paris, France. Weekly newsletter.

Pacific Affairs: An International Review of Asia and the Pacific, University of British Columbia, Vancouver, BC V6T 1W5, Canada. Quarterly academic journal.

Pacific Islands Monthly, Pacific Publications (Aust.), 76 Clarence St., Sydney, NSW 2000, Australia. Monthly news magazine.

PHILIPPINES

Communications, Mindanao Interfaith People's Conference Secretariate, P.O. Box 501, Davao City, Philippines. Quarterly magazine; social justice perspective.

CTF Bulletin, Congress Task Force, Coalition Against the Marcos Dictatorship, 1322 18 St., NW, Rm. 44, Washington, DC 20036. Bimonthly newsletter; progressive political point of view.

Katarungan, Ecumenical Movement for Justice and Peace, Suite 704, Insurance Bldg., 633 Gen. Luna St., Intramuros, Manila, Philippines. Bimonthly newsletter; progressive Christian point of view.

Philippine Labor Alert, Philippine Workers Support Committee, P.O. Box 11208, Moiliili Station, Honolulu, HI 96828. Bimonthly newsletter; progressive political point of view.

Philippine Labor Monitor, Institute for Labor Research and Documentation, CBS-83, MCPO, Makati, Manila, Philippines. Quarterly magazine; progressive political point of view.

Philippines Newswatch, Philippines Resource Centre, P.O. Box 5, 124 Napier St., Fitzroy, Victoria 3065, Australia. Monthly news service; progressive political point of view.

Political Detainees Update, Task Force Detainees of the Philippines, Association of Major Religious Superiors of the Philippines, 214 N. Domingo St., San Juan, Metro Manila, Philippines. Biweekly newsletter; Christian perspective.

Taliba, Coalition against the Marcos Dictatorship/Philippine Solidarity Network, P.O. Box 173, Oakland, CA 94663. Occasional newsletter; progressive political point of view.

THAILAND

Human Rights in Thailand Report, Coordinating Group for Religion in Society, 59 Soi Srisawad, Pradipat Rd., Bangkok 4, Thailand. Quarterly newsletter; Christian perspective.

INFORMATION SOURCES

For the most part establishment news magazine and academic journals have been omitted from the periodical list in this directory. For information on periodicals of that nature, readers should consult the bibliographies, guides, and reference books described above (pp. 34–40).

See also:

The Far East and Australasia 1984–85. London: Europa Publications. See p. 38–39 above.

The sixteenth edition of this reference book contains a select bibliography of over 160 periodicals from around the world on Asia and the Pacific (see pp. 89-94). Each entry contains founding date, address, frequency of publication, and editor's name.

Oxbridge Directory of Ethnic Periodicals. Edited by Patricia Hagood. New York: Oxbridge Communications, 1979. Index.

This directory covers U.S. and Canadian newspapers, magazines, newsletters, directories, yearbooks, and bibliographies with information on more than seventy ethnic groups. Entries include name, publisher, address, and—in most cases—additional data regarding frequency, subscription rate, and so forth.

The IMS Ayer Directory of Publications. Fort Washington, Penn.: IMS Communications, annual.

Ulrich's International Periodicals Directory. 2 vols. New York and London: R. R. Bowker, annual.

The above are the two standard library reference guides for information on foreign and domestic periodicals.

See also these two publications from Third World Resources:

Third World Resource Directory: A Guide to Organizations and Publications. Edited by Thomas P. Fenton and Mary J. Heffron. Maryknoll, N.Y.: Orbis Books, 1984. 304pp. $17.95, plus $1.50 shipping and handling. Illustrations, indexes. Available from Orbis Books, Maryknoll, NY 10545, or from Third World Resources, 464 19 St., Oakland CA 94612.

The periodicals section (pp. 22–26) and other resources section (pp. 33–36) of the Third World chapter are noteworthy, as is the entire printed resources section of the chapter on Asia and the Pacific (pp. 68–71). Cross-references in those sections direct readers to entries in other chapters (e.g., on women or human rights) that are related to Asia and the Pacific.

Third World Resources: A Quarterly Review of Resources from and about the Third World. 4 issues/year. Newsletter. 28cm. 16pp. $25/year (organizational subscription), $25/two years (individual subscription). Inquire for overseas rates. Subscriptions are available on a calendar-year basis only. Write: Third World Resources, 464 19 St., Oakland, CA 94612.

4

Pamphlets and Articles

The aim of this chapter is to present information about printed resource materials that are self-contained (usually an entire issue of a magazine on one topic), brief, inexpensive, and easily available—often at bulkrates.

The dividing line between a book and a pamphlet (or booklet) is a thin one at times. The rule of thumb used to distinguish between the two is: bound printed materials that numbered less than one hundred pages and/or were priced at less than $5.00 are listed in the pamphlets and articles chapter. Admittedly this dividing line is arbitrary, and it is hoped that no author will be offended that her/his work is classed as a "pamphlet." Resources in this chapter are no less important because they are concise.

This chapter is divided into three parts: annotated entries, supplementary list of pamphlets and articles, and sources of additional information on pamphlets and articles.

Each **annotated entry** includes: title; author(s); publisher; periodical name; publication data (volume, number, date); number of pages; price; keyword description of format; and description of content.

Pamphlets and articles in the **supplementary list** (pp. 75–80) are grouped under these headings: General Asia and Pacific; Bangladesh; East Timor; Indonesia; Kampuchea; Korea; Pakistan; Philippines; and Sri Lanka. Entries in this section include title; author(s); publisher; name of periodical; date; number of pages; and price.

The **information sources** section (p. 80) provides an annotated list of directories and guides that contain the names of other articles related to Asia and the Pacific.

The titles of all the entries in this chapter are integrated into the titles index at the back of the directory. See the organizations index for addresses of publishers and distributors that appear in this chapter. (Note that whenever the names of the publisher and the periodical are identical, the names will appear in both the titles and organizations indexes.)

ANNOTATED ENTRIES

Agriculture in Indochina: Is There Growth after Equity? Southeast Asia Resource Center. *Southeast Asia Chronicle* 87, December 1982. 30pp. $2.50. Photographs, notes, illustrations. Available from the Asia Resource Center (Washington, D.C.)

This issue of the *Chronicle* describes and analyzes some of the steps that were being taken (in 1982) in Vietnam and Kampuchea to meet the twin challenges of agricultural productivity and equitable distribution of food: "Agriculture must become more productive to feed a growing population, an increasing proportion of which does not produce its own food, and the products must be so distributed that people can meet their basic needs." The editors contrast this experience in the socialist countries with that of the capitalist-led countries of Southeast Asia (see issue no. 86 on agriculture in the member countries of the Association of Southeast Asian Nations).

Contents: "Vietnam Remaps Its Road to Socialist Development" by Christine White; "Focus on Nutrition" by Beatrice Eisman; "The IMF and Socialist Construction in Vietnam" by Walden Bello; "Working for the Basics in Kampuchea" by Sophie Quinn-Judge.

America's Missing: A Look behind the Numbers. Bill Herod. Center for International Policy, Indochina Project. *Indochina Issues* 54, February 1985. 8pp. $1. Map.

"Twelve years after the Paris peace agreement was signed and a decade after the collapse of the Saigon government, the issue of America's missing-in-action (MIAs) remains central to American public perceptions and official policies toward Vietnam and Laos," writes Bill Herod, a Washington-based consultant on Indochina for Church World Service. Herod describes how the Reagan administration and organizations such as the National League of Families of American Prisoners and Missing in Southeast Asia have represented and misrepresented this issue to the American people, and he contrasts Washington's less-than-cooperative attitude with actions taken by the Vietnam Veterans of America and the Australian government.

"Asia Askew: U.S. Best Sellers on Asia, 1931–1980." Daniel B. Ramsdell. *Bulletin of Concerned Asian Scholars* 15, no. 4 (1983). 23pp. $6 for entire issue. Illustrations, notes, figures, appendices.

After twenty years of teaching American college students about Asia, Daniel Ramsdell concludes that "acceptance of my information on Asia (and other less familiar parts of the world) was determined mainly by the degree to which my statements conformed to [the students'] existing notions and beliefs." Professor Ramsdell searched for the source of his students' "impressionistic misinformation and facile generalizations about Asia" in Asia-related books produced by 178 best-selling U.S. authors from 1931–80. Included in the list of authors are Pearl Buck, Lin Yutang, James Michener, James Clavell, and John Masters. Ramsdell underlines the racism, sexism, and patronizing clichés in the works of all of these authors and classifies each of the titles in terms of popularity, content, and impact.

Beyond Hiroshima: Nuclear Energy in East Asia. Peter Neu. Center for the Progress of Peoples. 1982. 51pp. $2. Map, illustrations, notes, table.

This popularly written booklet offers a critical perspective on the development of nuclear power in Asia. The author analyzes the energy-need projections of governments in Taiwan, the Philippines, and South Korea and raises concerns about the economics and advisability of meeting these needs through nuclear energy. The booklet closes with guidelines for future debate on nuclear power in Asia.

Beyond Stereotypes: Asian Women in Development. Southeast Asia Resource Center. *Southeast Asia Chronicle* 96, January 1985. 34pp. $2.50. Photographs, tables, resource guide, notes, complete backlist of *Southeast Asia Chronicle* (July 1971 through January 1985, the final issue). Available from the Asia Resource Center (Washington, D.C.) and the Philippine Resource Center (Berkeley, Calif.).

"Our treatment of Asian women caught in the process called development," say the editors of this issue of the *Chronicle,* "is not a litany of distress for victims. Certainly, articles in this issue describe exploitation and hardship, but they also highlight the resourcefulness and personal dignity with which women throughout Asia are responding to their circumstances."

Contents: "Industrialization and Prostitution in Southeast Asia" by Aihwa Ong; "In Pursuit of an Illusion: Thai Women in Europe" and "Three Women" by Siriporn Skrobanek; "Friends of Women" by Chris Jenkins; "Making a Living: South Korean Women in Commerce" by Pilwhat Chang-Michell; "Offering Support: Maternity Leave and Childcare" by Vu Thi Chin; and "From Birth Control to Population Control" by Lynn Duggan.

Cambodia and Vietnam: Costs of the Alliance. Murray Hiebert. Center for International Policy, Indochina Project. *Indochina Issues* 46, May 1984. 8pp. $1. Map.

Drawing on interviews conducted during two trips to Kampuchea in early 1984, Murray Hiebert describes various aspects of life in that wartorn country. Hiebert analyzes the political, military, and economic relations between the Vietnamese and the government of Heng Samrin, and he speculates about future cooperation among the three countries of Indochina.

Collision Course at Kwajalein: Marshall Islanders in the Shadow of the Bomb. Giff Johnson. Pacific Concerns Resource Center. 1984. 72pp. Europe, Asia, Pacific: $9.50; United States, Canada, Micronesia: $7.95. Airmail postage included. Bibliography, photographs, maps, notes, illustrations, resources list.

Collision Course is about the devastating impact of the nuclear arms race on the Marshallese people and the leading role these remote Pacific islands have played in developing America's nuclear arsenal. The author, a knowledgeable and dedicated activist on Pacific-Asian issues, tells the story of the Marshallese people and then describes the nuclear weapons systems being developed or planned for testing at the Kwajalein Missile Range. Johnson's aim is "to draw attention to destabilizing nuclear innovations and critical human rights problems that have gone virtually unnoticed at the Kwajalein Missile Range."

Contracts in Vietnam: More Rice, New Problems. Murray Hiebert. Center for International Policy, Indochina Project. *Indochina Issues* 48, July 1984. 8pp. $1. Map.

This article describes how economic reforms in rural Vietnam—especially the "contract system" introduced in 1981—have spurred production of rice, fish, and other food. These reforms, however, have given rise to concern on the part of some officials that giving farmers control over the disposition of their surplus production (under terms of the contract system) will lead to a breakdown in the cooperative system of production and distribution of agricultural goods.

Linda Gibson Hiebert, codirector of the Indochina Project, contributes to this issue an article on the re-education camps she visited in Vietnam in January 1984 and on the possibility that Hanoi is softening its earlier "all-or-nothing" position on the release of inmates of these camps to the United States.

Dealing with Hanoi: What Washington Can Do. Anthony Lake. Center for International Policy, Indochina Project. *Indochina Issues* 49, August 1984. 8pp. $1.

In January 1984, Anthony Lake returned to Vietnam where he had been stationed in the foreign service in 1963–65. *In Dealing with Hanoi* Lake writes about the policy implications of what he and two other former U.S. government officials learned during their trip. He analyzes the strategic interests of all the countries involved in the affairs of Indochina, weighs the pros and cons of U.S. normalization of relations with Hanoi, and concludes with a list of four positive steps that Washington could take to prepare the way for normalization. These include a relaxing of the restrictions currently placed on private, voluntary organizations in their efforts to provide small-scale help to people in Vietnam and Cambodia.

Diego Garcia: A Contrast to the Falklands. John Madeley. Minority Rights Group. Report no. 54. February 1985. Rev. ed. 16pp. $3.95. Map, notes, appendixes, bibliography, resources.

For over two centuries the Ilois people inhabited the islands of the Chagos Archipelago in the Indian Ocean. They lived a simple, largely self-sufficient life as fishers and farmers. Although the islands were administered by the British government, the politics of colonialism was remote from the daily lives of the Ilois people. In 1966 all this changed. While all the other islands in the British Ocean Territories were granted independence, Diego Garcia was not included. Instead it was leased to the United States as a military base. The Ilois were evacuated and transported to Mauritius where they were left to live—and die—in the slums of Port Louis without food, money, housing, or compensation. Today Diego Garcia is the largest U.S. military base in the Indian Ocean and the Ilois are not allowed to return—either to live or visit.

Diego Garcia tells the story of the Ilois, their displacement from their home islands, and their struggle for recognition and justice.

East Timor. Catholic Institute for International Relations. *Comment* 31, January 1982. 12pp. Free with membership in CIIR: £10.00 overseas airmail for 5 issues/year.

This pamphlet—one in CIIR's readable and attractive *Comment* series—traces developments leading up to the invasion of the former Portuguese colony of East Timor by the armed forces of Indonesia on December 7, 1975, and describes activities since that time in the United Nations and in the capital cities of Indonesia's allies.

"The economic and strategic interests of the major Western powers in Indonesia make it unlikely that they will of their own accord take up the case of East Timor," CIIR concludes. "This places an even greater responsibility on non-governmental organizations and the press," they state, "to ensure that [East Timor] is not forgotten."

"East Timor: The Responsibility of the United States." Richard W. Franke. *Bulletin of Concerned Asian Scholars* 15, no. 2 (1983). 16pp. $6 for entire issue. Map, photographs, notes, table.

In this paper, presented at the Permanent Peoples' Tribunal on East Timor (June 1981), the author addresses six principal areas of U.S. responsibility for events in East Timor. These are: (1) general U.S. strategy in Asia; (2) U.S. role in destabilizing the Sukarno government; (3) U.S. military aid during the invasion of East Timor in December 1975; (4) U.S. diplomatic support for the Suharto regime during the invasion; (5) U.S. government misrepresentation of events in East Timor; and (6) U.S. government help to "the Indonesian regime to hold hostage even the humanitarian aid programs that might at least ease some of the material suffering of the East Timorese people at the present time."

East Timor: Unfinished Business. Southeast Asia Resource Center. *Southeast Asia Chronicle* 94, June 1984. 28pp. $2.50. Photographs, illustrations, notes, resource guide. Available from the Asia Resource Center (Washington, D.C.).

This issue of the *Chronicle* is a celebration of the "resurrection" of Fretilin, the principal resistance force to Indonesian occupation of East Timor. "Fretilin has returned from near annihilation to pose a serious threat to the Indonesian occupation," write the editors. "Even if Fretilin cannot totally defeat the Indonesian military, it is steadily increasing the military and diplomatic costs of the occupation. At some point," they conclude, "that cost will become unbearable even for the Indonesian military dictatorship."

Contents (partial): "Fretilin: Death and Resurrection" by Australian journalist Denis Freney; "The Occupation" by Joel Rocamora and Will Seaman; and "East Timor and Diplomatic Pragmatism" by M. A. Browning and Susan Vitka. The issue includes a one-page annotated listing of books, publications, and organizations concerned with East Timor.

ORPHAN

HOLD
DO NOT SHIP

H1–000000000642

ISBN 9780883445280

CLIENT	Alternate Sourcing
STATION	TPP Receiving Station 01
HELD	2026–10–12 13:42

SHELF

If its order arrives, scan this label at a receiving station.

See also: *East Timor: Beyond Hunger.* Southeast Asia Resource Center. *Southeast Asia Chronicle 74,* August 1980. Available from the Asia Resource Center (Washington, D.C.).

400 Year War: Moro Struggle in the Philippines. Southeast Asia Resource Center. *Southeast Asia Chronicle* 82, February 1982. 30pp. $2.50. Photographs, map. Available from the Asia Resource Center (Washington, D.C.) and the Philippine Resource Center (Berkeley, Calif.).

This issue of the *Chronicle* is devoted entirely to an analysis by Rutgers University political sociologist Aijaz Ahmad of the Moro rebellion in the southern Philippines, a war Ahmad labels as "massive, brutal, and almost altogether secret—for everyone except the victims."

"Americans fought a bitter war against the Moros for a decade (1903–13)," Professor Ahmad explains, "and American corporations have owned plantations in Mindanao since 1919." Still, he says, the world barely acknowledges the existence of these roughly two million Filipinos who belong to the Moro tradition. Ahmad describes both the impact of colonialism and imperialism on the Moro people and the full-scale war presently being waged against the Muslims.

Health Care in Southeast Asia. Southeast Asia Resource Center. *Southeast Asia Chronicle* 84, June 1982. 34pp. $2.50. Bibliography, photographs, notes, tables, illustrations. Available from the Asia Resource Center (Washington, D.C.).

Southeast Asia, together with East Asia, had the highest economic growth rate in the world in the 1970s. Yet during this period, write the editors of this issue of the *Chronicle,* "living conditions, including the health of the vast majority of the people of the region, have steadily deteriorated." "If economic growth does not result in better health," they ask, "what does growth mean?"

Contents (partial): "Public Health and Imperialism: Early Rockefeller Programs at Home and Abroad" adapted from a longer article by Dr. E. Richard Brown; "The (Rockefeller) Foundation Knows Best: Early Medical Education in Thailand" extracted from an article by Peter J. Donaldson; "Health Policy in ASEAN: Addressing Human Needs or Protecting the Status-quo?" by Linda Golley; "Promoting Health, Fighting a Revolution" by Joel Rocamora; "Visit to a (Vietnamese) Commune Clinic" by Alex Marshall.

Human Rights Activism: Some Asian Experiences and Perspectives. Asian Coalition of Human Rights Organizations. Published in cooperation with the International Center for Law in Development. June 1984. 80pp. $8, plus postage. Available from Learning Resources in International Studies, c/o Council on International and Public Affairs, 777 United Nations Plaza, Suite 9A, New York, NY 10017.

This booklet provides an overview of the human rights situation in the Asian region and then devotes a section to each of these countries: Sri Lanka, India, Bangladesh, Nepal, Australia, Indonesia, the Philippines, and Malaysia. A concluding section contains suggestions for some approaches to human rights activism in Asia.

Human Rights Situation and Militarization in the Philippines: Trends and Analysis 1984. 1985. 27pp. $3. Available from the Philippine Resource Center (Berkeley, Calif.).

The information presented in this pamphlet comes mainly from the findings of a thirteen-member fact-finding mission that traveled throughout the Philippines in September 1984. Additional data were also solicited from human rights groups, especially on the topics and areas not exhaustively covered by the fact-finding teams.

The project was organized by local and regional human rights organizations such as the Task Force Detainees of the Philippines, Medical Action Group, Ecumenical Partnership for International Concerns—Philippines, and the Human Rights Office of the National Council of Churches of the Philippines.

Topics covered include: the government's counterinsurgency and pacification drives, violations of human rights, the legal system, and the response of the people. Two appendixes provide data on foreign military aid to the Philippines and the full text of the resolutions and recommendations of the mission.

Hunger in Cambodia: Getting beyond Relief. John Spragens, Jr. Center for International Policy, Indochina Project. *Indochina Issues* 43, February 1984. 6pp. $1.

"Restrictions on United States and United Nations aid to Cambodia make it difficult for the country to move beyond the level of precarious subsistence," writes *Indochina Issues* editor John Spragens. "When its main crop is hit by floods and droughts, as it was [in 1983]," Spragens says, "Cambodia is faced with the prospects of severe food shortages. Even if the United States is not prepared to change its basic aid policies, it can make a significant contribution to helping the people of Cambodia through this immediate crisis."

Invisible Control: Management Control of Workers in a U.S. Electronics Company. Christina Tse. Center for the Progress of Peoples. 1981. 70pp. $2.50. Statistical tables, notes, bibliography.

"The present project," according to its director, "explores the relationship between workers and management in a foreign-based electronics firm [Fairchild Semiconductor]. . . . The project takes a comparative approach and seeks to enter into the reality of workers in two Asian countries: Korea and Hongkong. We examine, compare, and analyse the labour-management mechanisms at work."

Through personal stories of workers in Korea and Hongkong the author shows how "the invisible mechanisms of control" tend "to inculcate in workers a value system which keeps them passive and keeps them from presenting a united front."

Iron Hand, Velvet Glove: Studies on Militarization in Five Critical Areas in the Philippines. Ecumenical Movement for Justice and Peace (Kilusan Para Sa Katarungan at Kapayapaan). *Background Information,* 1980/2. 70pp. Inquire for price. Map, tables, appendixes. Available from the Commission of the Churches on International Affairs, World Council of Churches, 150 route de Ferney, 1211 Geneva 20, Switzerland.

This study of militarization in five areas of the Philippines (Samar, Bataan, Davao, Cagayan, and Abra) establishes direct ties between militarization and (1) the violation of human rights and (2) transnational corporations. In addition, *Iron Hand, Velvet Glove* presents "peasants, urban and rural workers, tribal Filipinos, and urban poor populations not merely as victims of repression and deception, but as people actively resisting unjust claims on their land, their properties, and their lives."

Japan in Southeast Asia: Co-Prosperity? Southeast Asia Resource Center. *Southeast Asia Chronicle* 88, February 1983. 26pp. $2.50. Photographs, illustrations, maps, tables, notes. Available from the Asia Resource Center (Washington, D.C.).

Martha Winnacker's introductory essay on the role that both the United States and Japan play in keeping the Pacific safe for capitalism sets the stage for studies of Japanese economic penetration into Indonesia, Malaysia, and the Philippines.

"Japanese capital in Southeast Asia functions in much the same way as American capital," the editors write, "although there are of course many particularities characteristic of each. While we take account of some of the particularities—especially in the description of one firm's management practices in Malaysia—we are more concerned to offer an introductory understanding of the way in which the two states work together to maintain capitalist dominance of the region."

Kampuchea Survives. . . . But What Now? Southeast Asia Resource Center. *Southeast Asia Chronicle* 77, February 1981. 32pp. $1.50. Map, advertisements, photographs, book reviews. Available from the Asia Resource Center (Washington, D.C.).

This issue of the *Chronicle* is designed "to reintroduce some of the complexities left out of too many press reports" about Kampuchea. "This is important," say the editors, "for the sake of the historical record. More than that, if we want to consider what can be done in the future, we need a broad-ranging picture of what has happened so far."

Contents: "Kampuchea 1980: Anatomy of a Crisis" by Stephen R. Heder; "When the Peasant War Triumphed" and "Why Is There Famine in Kampuchea?" by Jan Myrdal; "Chamcar Loeu: A Gradual Recovery" by Paul Quinn-Judge; "Kampuchea's Choices for Survival" by Ben Kiernan.

See also: *The Kampuchea Debate.* Southeast Asia Resource Center. *Southeast Asia Chronicle* 79, August 1981. 30pp. $2.50. Photographs, illustration, bibliography. Available from the Asia Resource Center (Washington, D.C.).

Korea: The Forgotten Struggle. Korea Support Committee. 1984. 20pp. $2.50. Illustrations, photographs, map, notes, resources. Available from the Korea Support Committee, P.O. Box 11425, Oakland, CA 94611.

This pamphlet offers a good introduction to the geography and history of Korea along with a critical analysis of U.S. involvement in South Korea. *The Forgotten Struggle* covers the Kwangju uprising, the South Korean labor movement, California's ties with South Korea, and nuclear power and weapons in South Korea.

Kwajalein: Home on the "Range." The Kwajalein Missile Range and

Operation Homecoming. Darlene Keju and Giff Johnson. *Pacific Magazine,* November/December 1982. 8pp. $1. Maps, photographs. Available from the Pacific Concerns Resource Center (Honolulu).

This reprint from *Pacific Magazine* describes the U.S. military base on Kwajalein Island—a missile testing range that "has perhaps contributed more to the nuclear arms race than any other spot on earth." The authors describe the disgraceful conditions that the Marshallese people are forced to live and work in on the nearby island of Ebeye, and they discuss Operation Homecoming and other means of resistance by the people.

Laos: A Long Walk Forward. Southeast Asia Resource Center. *Southeast Asia Chronicle* 91, October 1983. 30pp. $2.50. Photographs, notes, resource guide. Available from the Asia Resource Center (Washington, D.C.).

This issue of the *Chronicle* examines developments in U.S.-Lao relations, religion in socialist Laos, the reasons behind the flight of the Hmong people from their native land, and the Lao people's efforts to rebuild their war-ravaged country along socialist lines. Jacqui Chagnon and Roger Rumpf, who lived and worked in Laos from 1978 to 1981, contributed a number of articles to this issue. Other contributors are: Wu Ruiming, an Asia-based freelance writer; Sombath Somphone, a Lao national and doctoral student at the University of Hawaii; and Linda and Titus Peachey, staff members in Laos of the Mennonite Central Committee.

This issue contains a five-page section of resources, "Dealing with Indochina: A Resource Guide," compiled by Kathryn Olney and Lee Esbenshade.

The Light and the Burning: A Witness to the Filipino Struggle. Derek Evans. United Church of Canada, BC Conference, Division of Global Concerns (1955 W. Fourth Ave., No. 200, Vancouver, BC V6J 1M7, Canada). 1982. 60pp. $4. Map, photographs, resource list.

"This is not a balanced report!" the author warns. "This report is irrevocably prejudiced by my own interests and hopelessly biased by my experiences, both of which are vested in the plight of the common people, in this case, of the Philippines."

"My purpose," Evans states, "is to share [with his Canadian audience] what I . . . discovered [during a trip to the Philippines in the winter of 1980] of the real 'other side,' the experience of the victims, the silent hidden ones. I present it here because this perspective of 'the people' is increasingly giving shape to the way in which the Church in Asia is coming to understand its own identity."

Losing Control: Towards an Understanding of Transnational Corporations in the Pacific Islands Context. James E. Winkler. Pacific Conference of Churches. 1982. 82pp. $4. Notes, illustrations, tables, maps, photographs. Available from Lotu Pasifika Productions, P.O. Box 208, Suva, Fiji.

In this eighty-two page booklet James Winkler builds a case in support of his contention that the Pacific Ocean represents a frontier that "is increasingly being exploited for food, mineral resources, and oil by the industrial nations and transnational corporations." "Thus," he concludes, "the island nations and their resources are being used to fulfill the needs of people in the West, not the people who actually live there."

Winkler gives a general description of transnational corporations and then examines their activities in the Pacific, concentrating on the mining, fishing, forestry, and tourism industries. He concludes with an exploration of alternatives and a discussion of the churches' role in defense of those exploited by these powerful corporations.

Marshall Islands: A Chronology, 1944–1983. Micronesia Support Committee. July 1983, 3rd ed. rev. 44pp. $3. Photographs, maps, bibliography. Available from the Pacific Concerns Resource Center (Honolulu).

This unique resource is divided into two sections: the first deals with the struggle of the Marshallese people to survive in exile, and the second describes the contamination and destruction of island homelands by the U.S. military.

The first section begins in February 1944 when U.S. forces captured the Enewetak and Kwajalein atolls from the Japanese, and it ends in late April 1983 with a U.S. official saying that the U.S. army is "planning to stick around Kwajalein for a long time" and that military and civilian communities should work out ways of getting along.

Section two opens with the U.S. bombing of Hiroshima and Nagasaki and then documents, in chronological order, the detonation of other U.S. nuclear weapons in the Pacific in the years since August 1945.

Militarism and Repression in the Philippines. Jim Zwick. Centre for Developing-Area Studies, McGill University (Macdonald-Harrington Building, 815 Sherbrooke St. W., Montreal, Quebec H3A 2K6, Canada). Working Paper Series, no. 31. 1982. 70pp. Canadian $2.50. Tables, notes, bibliography.

The author selected the Philippines for his study of militarism and repression "because, despite several factors which differentiate it from other Third World countries in which repressive regimes exist, [the Philippines] is plagued by economic, social, and political problems facing nearly all developing countries." "Thus," he says, ". . . . its internal instability and external dependence are characteristic features of development and militarism in many other countries. Also, like its Southeast Asian neighbours and many other former colonies in Latin America and Africa, the Philippines, with the declaration of martial law in September of 1972, has made the transition from a western-style democracy to authoritarian rule."

A postscript, written on May 25, 1982, considers the ways in which the Reagan election and the formal lifting of martial law by President Marcos affected militarism and repression in the Philippines.

Monster in Morong: The Dreadful Tale of the Bataan-Westinghouse Nuclear Plant in the Philippines. Jorgé Emmanuel. Friends of the Filipino People and the Alliance for Philippine Concerns. June 1984. 4pp. 25 cents. Action suggestions, organizational listings, recommended readings.

This is the incredible story of the construction of the Bataan Nuclear

Power Plant (in Morong, Bataan)—reputed to be "one of the most expensive nuclear facilities of its size and one of the most dangerous in the world." "It is threatened," writes Emmanuel, "by possible volcanic eruptions, severe earthquakes, and plagued by faulty design problems." Emmanuel describes the role that Westinghouse and the U.S. Export-Import Bank played in the promotion, design, and construction of this plant. *Monster in Morong* also covers: who benefits from the Bataan facility, the relationship between the BNPP and the two U.S. bases in the Philippines, and the birth of the Nuclear Free Philippines Coalition in January 1981.

Muroroa: The Dirtiest Island in the Pacific Will Be One-Hundred Bombs Old in 1984. Marie-Thérèse and Bengt Danielsson. December 1983. 18pp. U.S., Canada, and Micronesia: $1.20; Europe: $1.90; Pacific and Asia: $2.10. Available from the Pacific Concerns Resource Center (Honolulu).

The Danielssons provide an updated report on the destruction that French nuclear weapons tests have caused at Muroroa. They cover as well the scientific missions sent to Muroroa by Australia and New Zealand.

Myth and Ideology in U.S. Foreign Policy: East Timor and El Salvador. Noam Chomsky. East Timor Human Rights Committee. 1982. 28pp. 60 cents. Bulk rates available. English and Spanish. Photographs, maps, illustrations, resource list.

In this speech delivered at a 1981 Yale University conference on the genocide in East Timor, MIT professor Noam Chomsky explains how the "U.S. ideological and propaganda system" (terms he uses to cover the mainstream media and the academic profession) structures the terms of debate and thus deflects the attention of the U.S. public away from substantive issues of U.S. intervention in East Timor, El Salvador, and other Third World areas. Using the example of East Timor, Chomsky suggests three ways people in the U.S. can free themselves from the prevailing system of propaganda and ideology, and he discusses U.S. responsibility for the situation in East Timor on three levels: the U.S. government, the U.S. press, and U.S. citizens.

Nuclear Issues in Asia and the Pacific. Thomas P. Fenton. *Maryknoll.* June-September 1985. 15pp. $2.50. Photographs, action guide. Available from Third World Resources (Oakland, Calif.).

This set of articles reprinted from the *Maryknoll* magazine surveys four critical issues related to nuclear energy and weapons in Asia and the Pacific: the proposed dumping of radioactive wastes in the Pacific; nuclear proliferation in South Asia; nuclear weapons testing; and the U.S.-sponsored construction of nuclear power plants in Asia.

Pacific Alert: Nuclear Arms and the New Militarism. Southeast Asia Resource Center. *Southeast Asia Chronicle* 95, November 1984. 30pp. $2.50. Photographs, notes, map, action guide, book reviews. Available from the Asia Resource Center (Washington, D.C.).

"A new Pacific is being forged in the struggle to turn back the threat of nuclear war and intervention," write the editors of *Pacific Alert.* "People are reaching across the ocean, from Manila to Hawaii, from Vanuatu to Tokyo, to form a community dedicated to a vision of the Pacific different from the current reality of false and repressive 'peace' imposed by a U.S. military bent on confrontation." This issue of the *Chronicle*—the product of a joint effort by Nautilus Pacific Action Research, U.S. Pacific Issues Network, and the Southeast Asia Resource Center—analyzes both the current realities of nuclear-tipped militarism and visions of a nuclear-free Pacific. Much of the material presented in this issue is drawn from *An American Lake: The Nuclear Peril in the Pacific* (p.27 above).

Pacific and Asian Americans. Board of Church and Society of the United Methodist Church (110 Maryland Ave., NE, Washington, DC 20002). *engage/social action* 11, no. 4, April 1983. 55pp. 10 cents. Order *e/sa forum*–92, no. CSE2092. Photographs, illustrations, organizational guide.

This forum on Pacific and Asian Americans contains a seven-page article on "Human Rights Hotspots in the Asian Homelands" by Pastor Lloyd K. Wake of San Francisco's Glide Memorial United Methodist Church. Wake surveys the entire region, but pays particular attention to human rights issues in South Korea, the Philippines, and Taiwan.

Palau: Self-Determination vs. Military Plans. Micronesia Support Committee. May 1983. 24pp. $1. Photographs, maps, illustrations, action guide, resource list. Available from the Pacific Concerns Resource Center (Honolulu).

Palau tells the story of how and why the people of the Republic of Palau voted (over U.S. objections) to effectively create a nuclear-free zone around their islands in the western Pacific. This pamphlet also contains a lengthy excerpt from an article by Giff Johnson in *AMPO* magazine: "Pentagon Stalks Micronesia: Strategic Interests vs. Self-Determination" *(AMPO: Japan-Asia Quarterly Review* 14, no. 4 [1982]). An eight-page reprint of the Johnson article is available from the Pacific Concerns Resource Center (Honolulu) for 50 cents.

Peasants, Packing Plants, and Plastic Wrappers: ASEAN's Agricultural Production. Southeast Asia Resource Center. *Southeast Asia Chronicle* 86, October 1982. 30pp. $2.50 Photographs, tables, notes, map, news update, advertisements. Available from the Asia Resource Center (Washington, D.C.).

This issue of the *Chronicle* examines the unequal power relationships between peasant agricultural producers in four Southeast Asian countries and those to whom they sell or for whom they labor: "the largest non-governmental organizations the world has ever known—transnational corporations based in the industrialized countries."

Contents: "Old Class Structures and New Crops" by Chayan Vaddhanaphuti and Martha Winnacker; "Food as Corporate Commodity" by Frederick F. Clairmonte and John Cavanagh; "Being a Peasant in Java" by Richard W. Franke.

Philippine Debt to Foreign Banks. John E. Lind. California/Nevada Interfaith Committee on Corporate Responsibility (220 Golden Gate Ave., 9th floor, San Francisco, CA 94101). November 1984. 26pp. $5. Illustrations, notes, figures, tables.

At the end of 1983 the Philippines owed $14.2 billion to foreign commercial banks; $6.5 billion of that amount was in the form of medium- and long-term debts—the funds used for critical capital investments. This NC–ICCR report identifies the borrowers and the foreign banks that hold 80 percent of these debts. It then studies the Philippine debt in the context of the financial crises of the 1980s.

Appendixes explain the procedure used in the bank lending survey and describe the way in which funds from lending institutions enter the Philippines.

The Philippines after Aquino, after Marcos? Southeast Asia Resource Center. *Southeast Asia Chronicle* 92, December 1983. 30pp. $2.50. Photographs, notes, illustrations, resource guide. Available from the Asia Resource Center (Washington, D.C.) and the Philippine Resource Center (Berkeley, Calif.).

Shortly after the assassination of Benigno Aquino the staff of the Southeast Asia Resource Center compiled this issue of the *Chronicle* to bare the known facts about Aquino's murder and to establish the political rationale for the direct involvement of President Marcos in the decision to assassinate Aquino. The tragic death of Ninoy Aquino is set in context in a lengthy description by Joel Rocamora of the main protagonists on the political scene in the Philippines today and in a study of the deteriorating economic situation in the Philippines by Robin Broad and John Cavanagh.

The Philippines in the 80s: From Normalization to Polarization. Southeast Asia Resource Center. *Southeast Asia Chronicle* 83, April 1982. 30pp. $2.50. Photographs, map, notes. Available from the Asia Resource Center (Washington, D.C.) and the Philippine Resource Center (Berkeley, Calif.).

Joel Rocamora launches this issue with a description of the political and military activities of the organization that by 1981 had become the leading force in the resistance to Ferdinand Marcos: the leftist National Democratic Front. Robert Rose follows with an on-the-scene account of life inside the New People's Army. Rocamora contributes two additional articles on the nature of U.S. support for the Marcos regime and the source of Manila's economic crisis. Mennonite Earl Martin describes the transfer of the "strategic hamlet" strategy from Vietnam to the southern Philippines, and Paul Hutchcroft, a staff member of Clergy and Laity Concerned, writes about life around the U.S. naval base at Subic Bay.

Power Relations in Rural Development: The Case of Bangladesh. Richard W. Timm, C.S.C. Center for the Progress of Peoples. 1983. 64pp. $2.50. Map, photographs, illustrations, statistical tables, notes.

"The naked power of the economic elite of the countryside ensures that they will get the lion's share of development," writes Richard Timm, a Catholic priest with over thirty years of experience in Bangladesh. "[The rural elite's] alliance with the political elite of the urban areas ensures that their benefits will not be lost, either through legislation or through any pressure for change in the status quo."

"How has this situation developed," Timm asks, "and what can be done about it? Will Bangladesh eventually be thrown out of the 'lifeboat' because it is such a huge liability? Though the situation may look desperate today, it was not always so. The reasons for the underdevelopment of

Bangladesh have to be clearly exposed before any change for the better is possible."

Timm's work is scholarly and is backed by years of experience in the field.

Seeds and Food Security. Sahabat Alam Malaysia (Friends of the Earth Malaysia). 1984. 85pp. $4. Photographs, illustrations, tables, notes, map, appendixes.

Seeds and Food Security critically weighs the gains and losses for Third World countries from the much-heralded Green Revolution. "Despite fairly impressive production increases," writes the president of Friends of the Earth Malaysia, "the socio-economic impact of the Green Revolution—in exacerbating income disparities in the countryside, benefiting disproportionately a small number of capitalist farmers, businessmen, and bureaucrats, and in failing to break the back of the rural poverty syndrome—is now well known."

The pamphlet moves from the well-known facts about the Green Revolution to the relatively unknown story of the monopoly control of the international seed industry by transnational corporations—a development the authors see as "threatening the well-being of subsistence farmers as well as the ecological heritage of the Third World."

Soft-Sell Socialism in Northeast Laos. Murray Hiebert. Center for International Policy, Indochina Project. *Indochina Issues* 50, September 1984. 8pp. $1. Map.

"When the United States began bombing Sam Neua [in northeastern Laos] in 1964," writes Murray Hiebert, "the revolutionaries and local people took shelter in the area's giant natural limestone caves. For the next eight years, a pharmaceutical factory, a tool workshop, a weaving mill, schools, and the revolutionary government operated out of these caves."

In this report on his 1984 trip to Sam Neua, the legendary headquarters of the Lao revolution, Hiebert observes that "the scars of war still remain. It seems that not a house, village, or bridge survived the bombing. . . .Rice fields are still pocked with craters." Reconstruction, however, is taking place—along socialist lines and with generous aid from the Vietnamese.

Linda Gibson Hiebert contributes to this issue an article on improvements in U.S.-Lao relations.

South Korea in Crisis: Danger or Opportunity? Bruce Cumings. From *SAIS Review,* Summer/Fall 1983. 16pp. $1.50. Available from North American Coalition for Human Rights in Korea (Washington, D.C.).

"South Korea," writes the author, "is now in the fifth year of a political-economic crisis. This crisis has four dimensions: economic structure, political regime, international environment, and elite-mass relations."

"Within each dimension," he explains, "there is a key problem: in the economy, sluggish exports amid a huge debt burden; in the polity, heightened authoritarianism with diminished legitimacy; in the world at large, troubles with old allies and antagonists as well as with new suitors and potential friends; and between elite and mass, a new mood that is least apparent and yet may be the worst of the problems."

Cumings, an associate professor of international studies at the University of Washington, examines the nature of South Korea's crisis and recommends policy options for the U.S. government.

South Korea: The People Who Live at the Bottom of the Society. Kim Ch'ung-Sik. From *AMPO* 15, no. 1, 1983. 4pp. 60 cents. Available from North American Coalition for Human Rights in Korea (Washington, D.C.).

Published originally in the *Tong-A Ilbo* newspaper on January 24, 1983, under the title "The Struggle of the Have-Nots to Survive," this short article takes readers on a walk down the back alleys of South Korea's capital city and along timeworn paths in the countryside to expose the harsh realities behind the facade of South Korea's "economic miracle." As evidence that the economic policies of the Chun Doo Hwan regime are failing the people of his country the author writes: "More than 5,000 used-bottle collectors, chewing gum peddlers, vagrants, and beggars collapsed and died on the streets of Seoul in 1981. Of these 2,500 were children, 1,600 adult men, and 1,000 adult women."

South Korean Political Development in the 1980s. Thomas Robinson. 1983. 60pp. $4.25. Available from North American Coalition for Human Rights in Korea (Washington, D.C.).

This lengthy paper is a wide-ranging analysis of the prospects for political change and economic development in South Korea under the leadership of the Chun Doo Hwan government. The author, from Georgetown University's School of Foreign Service, examines the country's political parties, the student movement, the church, the press, the labor movement, and other forces for social change in South Korea. He draws no conclusions, but does offer various scenarios for development through the remainder of the 1980s.

"Teaching the Vietnam War: Objectivity in the Classroom." Stephen Vlastos. *Bulletin of Concerned Asian Scholars* 16, no. 4 (1984). 3pp. $6 for entire issue.

"Unlike my other courses on Asian history," writes University of Iowa professor Vlastos, "teaching the Vietnam war has brought me face to face with the issue of objectivity in the classroom." Vlastos posits three reasons why "students feel that courses on the Vietnam war are not likely to be purely academic," criticizes popular conceptions of objectivity in the classroom, and then offers his strategies for uncovering the values "that inform historical discourse" about the war in Vietnam.

See also: *Old Wine in New Bottles: "Reinterpreting" the Vietnam War.* Marilyn Blatt Young. *Southeast Asia Chronicle* 93, April 1984 (p. 77).

Terror In Paradise: The Philippines and East Asia as Theatres of Intervention and Nuclear War. Jorgé Emmanuel. Friends of the Filipino People and Alliance for Philippine Concerns. July 1984. 16pp. $1. Notes.

Why does the United States maintain over five hundred military installations in the East Asia–Pacific region? Why has the the U.S. military deployed over three thousand tactical nuclear weapons in Asia and the Pacific? Jorgé Emmanuel, of the Alliance for Philippine Concerns, addresses these questions by focusing on the role and function of the U.S.

bases in the Philippines. Emmanuel assesses the human costs of U.S. military installations in the region and describes steps being taken to create a nuclear free and independent Pacific.

Thailand: The Challenge of the 1980s. Southeast Asia Resource Center. *Southeast Asia Chronicle* 80, October 1981. 30pp. $2.50. Photographs, notes, illustrations, book reviews, advertisements, news update. Available from the Asia Resource Center (Washington, D.C.).

"Thailand has become a key player in the reassertion of an activist American role in East and Southeast Asia. Yet," write the editors of this issue of the *Chronicle,* "there has been little attention given to the internal crises which confront Thailand in the 1980s, despite the April (1981) coup attempt which threatened to explode into full-scale civil war."

Two Thailand specialists at the Southeast Asia Resource Center give the internal crises in Thailand the attention they deserve. Martha Winnacker writes on the competition for power among various establishment political factions in Thailand: "The Political Contest: More Than Cliques, Less Than Parties" and Santi Mingmongkol analyzes the crises that beset the Communist Party of Thailand in 1979–81: "Thai Communists into the 1980s."

This issue also contains excerpts from David Morrell's March 1981 congressional testimony urging an embargo on further U.S. arms supplies to Thailand.

Tourism: Selling Southeast Asia. Southeast Asia Resource Center. *Southeast Asia Chronicle* 78, April 1981. 38pp. $1.50. Photographs, illustrations, figures, notes, action guide, advertisements. Available from the Asia Resource Center (Washington, D.C.).

Tourism: Selling Southeast Asia is a major investigation of the multibillion dollar industry that brings over ten million visitors to East and Southeast Asia every year. "Asian governments and international financial institutions," write the editors, "view tourism as a 'strategic industry' in the export-oriented development of the region, allocating large budgets for national airlines, advertising, infrastructure, and hotel construction."

Articles by Robert Wood, Margaret Glenny, Rachael Grossman, Linda Richter, Pasuk Phongpaichit, Santi Mingmonkol, Patty Lee, and Indonesian poet Rendra evaluate the impact of this strategic industry on the people of Southeast Asia, particularly those in Thailand, Indonesia, and the Philippines.

Transnational Corporations in Asia. Thomas P. Fenton. *Maryknoll.* March-June 1982. 25pp. $2.50. Photographs, chart. Available from Third World Resources (Oakland, Calif.).

In this series of four articles reprinted from the *Maryknoll* magazine, Thomas Fenton describes and analyzes the impact of plant closings in the United States and foreign investment in Asia. Topics covered include: wages paid Asian workers, efforts to unionize in Asia, the profitability of U.S investments overseas, the shutdown of profit-making plants in the United States, and the costs—to Americans and Asians—of U.S. foreign investments.

Unofficial White Paper on the Kwangju Uprising. Korea Support Committee. 1982. 51pp. $4.

This paper summarizes the day-to-day events of the May 1980 uprising in the South Korean city of Kwangju and details the repressive and murderous actions of the South Korean government and military.

See also: *Peoples' Uprising in Kwangju.* Pacific-Asia Resource Center (Tokyo). September 1982.

U.S. Military Bases in the Philippines. Southeast Asia Resource Center and Campaign against Military Intervention in the Philippines, c/o Clergy and Laity Concerned (198 Broadway, New York, NY 10038). *Southeast Asia Chronicle* 89, April 1983. 34pp. $2.50. Photographs, maps, illustrations, notes, tables, chronology, resource list, advertisements. Available from the Asia Resource Center (Washington, D.C.) and the Philippine Resource Center (Berkeley, Calif.).

Articles in this issue of the *Chronicle* describe how U.S. military bases in the Philippines "hold the Filipino people hostage to the strategic interests of the United States" and how the bases are being used by the Reagan administration "to justify continued military and economic assistance to a regime that has been universally condemned as a notorious human rights violator."

Contents: "Springboards for Intervention, Instruments for Nuclear War" by Walden Bello; "Rapid Extinction: The Consequences of a Nuclear Attack on the Philippines" by Jorgé Emmanuel; "This is Whose Land? The 'Squatter Problem' at Clark" by Paul Hutchcroft; "Crumbs from the Military Table" by Earl Martin; "U.S. Bases, U.S. Bosses: Filipino Workers at Clark and Subic" by Paul Hutchcroft; and "For Sale: Girls" by Linda Golley.

Vietnam and the Soviets: A Tighter Alliance. John Spragens, Jr. Center for International Policy, Indochina Project. *Indochina Issues* 51, November 1984. 8pp. $1. Map.

"The United States and its allies in Asia say they are concerned about a growing Soviet military threat operating from bases in Vietnam," writes the author of this article. "But faced with continuing hostility from Washington and Peking, Hanoi sees little alternative to its ties with the Soviet Union."

Indochina Issues editor Spragens describes the nature of Soviet installations in Vietnam ("There is absolutely no comparison between what the Soviets have in Vietnam and what the U.S. has in the Philippines," he quotes one Western diplomat as saying), and he offers reasons why "the United States has taken few steps to offer Vietnam an alternative to the Soviet alliance."

See also: *Vietnam-China Split: Old Ties Remain.* Paul Quinn-Judge. Center for International Policy, Indochina Project. *Indochina Issues* 53, January 1985. 8pp. $1. Map.

Vietnam Is Still with Us. Southeast Asia Resource Center. *Southeast Asia Chronicle* 85, August 1982. 30pp. $2.50. Photographs, illustrations, charts, news update, advertisements. Available from the Asia Resource Center (Washington, D.C.).

"Vietnam is still with us," write the editors of this issue of the *Chronicle*. "Today, 'Vietnam' is the continuing agony of veterans unable to reconcile the realities of a brutal war with a home country opposed to, or worse, indifferent to that war. 'Vietnam' is half a million Indochinese refugees struggling to rebuild shattered lives in a strange land. 'Vietnam' is the cruel manipulation of the hopes of [Missing-in-Action] families. And 'Vietnam' is the continuing effort to understand and define the United States' role in the world." In addition to articles on these aspects of the continuing war, the issue contains an article by Alex West on the ways in which former Saigon military and police officers intimidate Vietnamese in the United States.

Vietnam: Some Reassessments. Southeast Asia Resource Center. *Southeast Asia Chronicle* 93, April 1984. 30pp. $2.50. Photographs, notes, illustration, advertisements, news update, book reviews. Available from the Asia Resource Center (Washington, D.C.).

"Reassessments" in the title of this issue has a dual reference: first, to the self-critical way in which the Vietnamese are redefining the possibilities for building socialism under conditions of poverty and limited access to international assistance, and, second, to the so-called new scholarship about the war in Vietnam.

Articles about the first of these reassessments are by Nguyen Khac Vien, editor of *Vietnam Courier*, Le Duc Tho, member of the Vietnam Communist Party's politburo, and Vo Van Kiet, head of Vietnam's State Planning Commission.

New York University history professor Marilyn Blatt Young addresses the second of the reassessments in her seven-page article: "Old Wine in New Bottles: 'Reinterpreting' the Vietnam War." Young critically analyzes an influential February 1983 article in the *New York Times Magazine* by former *Times* correspondent Fox Butterfield: "The New Vietnam Scholarship: Challenging the Old Passions." "A careful reading of Butterfield's essay," she writes, "and of the books on which he claims to have reached his conclusions, provides a summary of what is known as 'revisionist' interpretation of the war." This interpretation she finds misleading and harmful.

Vietnam: The Habit of War. Robert Archer. Catholic Institute for International Relations. 1983. 54pp. £1.25, plus postage. Maps, photographs.

This booklet analyzes the factors that are preventing Vietnam from being able to reconcile its people and rebuild its devastated economy. The author is critical of the Vietnamese government's "intolerance," but he is equally critical of the embargo on aid imposed by the United States and other Western powers. He recognizes that the country lacks the human and economic resources necessary for reconstruction and argues that the Vietnamese people should not be made to suffer for problems caused "by the shortcomings and ambitions of their own and foreign governments."

The World Bank. Southeast Asia Resource Center. *Southeast Asia Chronicle* 81, December 1981. 30pp. $2.50. Photographs, notes, news update, book reviews, advertisements. Available from the Asia Resource Center (Washington, D.C.).

"Reagan administration people have been critical of the World Bank for its 'failure' to promote U.S. economic interests," say the editors of *The World Bank*. "The example of Southeast Asia," they continue, "shows, on the contrary, that the Bank has not only pushed these interests all along, it initiated programs (in Thailand, Indonesia, and the Philippines) that greatly increased its leverage on behalf of these interests before Reagan came to office." Articles by Walden Bello and Robin Broad demonstrate this belief in the case of the Philippines, while John Kelly and Joel Rocamora focus on Indonesia and Santi Mingmongkol studies the World Bank in Thailand.

SUPPLEMENTARY LIST OF PAMPHLETS AND ARTICLES

GENERAL ASIA AND PACIFIC

Becoming the Church of the Poor in Asia. Bishop Julio X. Labayen. Six Roman Catholic agencies. *Church in the World* 19, 1985. 8pp. Available from Catholic Institute for International Relations (London).

Pacific Tourism: Contrasts in Values and Expectations. Cynthia Z. Biddlecomb. 1981. 61pp. Available from Lotu Pasifika, P.O. Box 208, Suva, Fiji.

BANGLADESH

Aid to Bangladesh: For Better or Worse? Michael Scott. Oxfam America. 1979. 30pp. $1.50.

Needless Hunger: Voices from a Bangladesh Village. Betsy Hartman and James Boyce. Institute for Food and Development Policy. 1979. 72pp. $3. Available from Oxfam America (Boston, Mass.).

EAST TIMOR

A Call for Justice. Indonesia East Timor Program. 1985. 8pp.

Hunger in East Timor. Indonesia East Timor Program. Forthcoming 1986.

INDONESIA

Indonesia and East Timor: An Organizer's Kit. 1985. $4, plus postage. Indonesia East Timor Program (Toronto).

Indonesia Country Profile. Published by a group of Roman Catholic international development agencies. 1982. 8pp. 50 cents. Available from Development and Peace (Toronto).

Women in Indonesia. Tabloid. Indonesia East Timor Program (Toronto).

KAMPUCHEA

Kampuchea Information Packet. Oxfam America. $3.50.

KOREA

Labor Rights Violations in the Republic of Korea. AFL–CIO, United Auto Workers, and the North American Coalition for Human Rights in Korea.

The Military Situation on the Korean Peninsula. Stephen D. Goose. *Korea Scope* 4, September 1984. 29pp. 80 cents, plus postage. Available from North American Coalition for Human Rights in Korea.

The Phoenix of 1984: A Vibrant Democratic Mass Movement Erupts in South Korea. Chang Paek-San. *AMPO* 1, 1985. 25pp. $1.25, plus postage. Available from North American Coalition for Human Rights in Korea.

Social Justice Index in Korea. Christian Institute for the Study of Justice and Development. 1981. 102pp.

PAKISTAN

Justice in Pakistan: A Report of a Mission of Inquiry. Lawyers Committee for International Human Rights and the Association of the Bar of the City of New York. July 1983. 46pp. $5.

PHILIPPINES

A Dialogue for Peace. Catholic Bishops' Conference of the Philippines. Six Roman Catholic agencies. *Church in the World* 15, 1983. 6pp. 20p. Available from Catholic Institute for International Relations (London).

Philippines Country Profile. Published by a group of Roman Catholic international development agencies. 1985. 8pp. 50 cents. Available from Development and Peace (Toronto).

Philippines Workers Information. Pamphlet. Contribution. Available from Development and Peace (Toronto).

SRI LANKA

Racism and the Authoritarian State. Special double issue of *Race & Class,* Summer 1984. $6. Available from the Institute of Race Relations, 247 Pentonville Rd., London N1 9NG, England.

A Struggle to Awaken. A. T. Ariyaatne. Sarvodaya Shramadana Movement. 1978. 69pp. $3.50. Available from Oxfam America (Boston, Mass.).

INFORMATION SOURCES

For information on additional pamphlets and articles related to Asia and the Pacific readers should (1) consult the periodicals listed in this directory that regularly feature a resource guide; (2) request a list of back issues of magazines such as *Indochina Issues* and *Southeast Asia Chronicle;* (3) see the bibliographies described above (pp. 34–40), especially the *Bibliography of Asian Studies* (p.34); (4) write for the publications catalogs of these organizations:

Cultural Survival, 11 Divinity Ave., Cambridge, MA 02138.

Lawyers Committee for International Human Rights, 36 W. 44 St., New York, NY 10036.

Minority Rights Group, 29 Craven St., London WC2, England, and 35 Claremont Ave., Rm. 4S, New York, NY 10027.

Pacific Concerns Resource Center, P.O. Box 27692, Honolulu, HI 96827.

Resource Center for Philippine Concerns, C.P.O. Box 1110, Tokyo 100–91, Japan.

Third World Studies Center, University of the Philippines, Rm. 428, Palma Hall Bldg., Diliman, Quezon City, Philippines.

U.S.-Pacific Issues Network, 1203 Smith Tower, Seattle, WA 98104.

See also these two publications from Third World Resources:

Third World Resource Directory: A Guide to Organizations and Publications. Edited by Thomas P. Fenton and Mary J. Heffron. Maryknoll, N.Y.: Orbis Books, 1984. 304pp. $17.95, plus $1.50 shipping and handling. Illustrations, indexes. Available from Orbis Books, Maryknoll, NY 10545, or from Third World Resources, 464 19 St., Oakland, CA 94612.

See the pamphlets and articles section (pp. 73–80) of the chapter on Asia and the Pacific, as well as the cross-referenced entries in other chapters such as those on women, transnational corporations, and human rights.

Third World Resources: A Quarterly Review of Resources from and about the Third World. 4 issues/year. Newsletter. 28cm. 16pp. $25/year (organizational subscription), $25/two years (individual subscription). Inquire for overseas rates. Subscriptions are available on a calendar-year basis only. Write: Third World Resources, 464 19 St., Oakland, CA 94612.

5

Audiovisuals

This chapter is divided into two parts: *visual resources* (films, filmstrips, slideshows, and videotapes), and *audio resources* (records and tapes). The visual resources section contains a supplementary list of audiovisuals and a description of additional sources of information. All audiovisuals are integrated into the title index at the back of the directory. See the organization index for the addresses of distributors listed in this chapter.

Visuals: Films, Filmstrips, Slideshows, Videotapes: Entries in this section include title, producer and director (when that information is available), format, distributor, and rental/purchase data. When the audiovisual is available from other distributors, their names have been given, but in deference to the rights of the principal distributor the often lower rental rates of those other distributors have been omitted. Interested parties are free, of course, to make their own inquiries.

Rental/purchase information should be taken as indicative only. Readers are urged to inquire about all fees and conditions before ordering an audiovisual. Some distributors have sliding price scales that depend upon the nature of an organization and the intended use of the audiovisual, so it is advisable to ask about discounts when making an inquiry.

It was impossible to preview all the audiovisuals included in this directory. In the case of audiovisuals that the editors were not able to evaluate personally, the distributors' descriptions of the audiovisuals have been quoted directly, indicating the source with the initials DIST (or AFSC, in the case of the American Friends Service Committee) at the end of the annotation. Annotations that conclude with the editors' initials (TFMH) are their own evaluations.

Care has been taken to select audiovisuals that appear to be worthy of consideration for use, but all interested parties are cautioned to arrange for previews of audiovisuals to determine their appropriateness for specific groups.

Audios: Records and Tapes: Because there are not many audio resources on the Asia and Pacific region, this section is organized by distributor rather than by resource titles. In this way the distributors of records and tapes can be introduced in a narrative form. In the process the types of resources they produce and/or distribute will be described—in a general way—and audio resources on the Asia and Pacific region, whenever these are available, will be highlighted.

The seven distributors described in this section are: Folkways, Great Atlantic Radio Conspiracy, Ladyslipper, Monitor, National Catholic Reporter, Pacifica, and Paredon.

Information Sources: In this section information is given about a number of reference works that can be used to locate further audiovisual materials.

VISUAL RESOURCES: FILMS, FILMSTRIPS, SLIDESHOWS, VIDEOTAPES

ANNOTATED ENTRIES

The ABC's of Philippine EPZ's. 1983. 28 minutes. Color slideshow with cassette tape. 142 color slides with script. Synapses. Rental: $15. Rental is for 10 days.

This slideshow describes—in a down-to-earth and entertaining manner—the complex social, political, and economic realities surrounding export processing zones (EPZs). The EPZs are special tax-exempt zones set aside for use by foreign corporations. In the words of one of the characters in this show: "EPZs are part of the Philippine government's open-door policy—an 'export promotion' program, which invites foreign, giant corporations to take advantage of our cheap labor and many exemptions from taxes and custom duties on imported machinery, raw materials, and equipment."

EPZ workers discuss the exploitative working conditions at German, Australian, Japanese, and U.S. factories in the zones and describe the terrible living conditions around the zones.

"Even if workers were given slightly better wages or allowed to form genuine trade unions," says one worker, "the fact is that these foreign corporations do not answer either the physical or basic human needs of the Filipino people!" With the picture of a Mattel-brand Barbie doll on the screen, he concludes: "The creative energies, labor force, and natural resources of the Philippines should first serve to feed, house, and clothe the people instead of housing and clothing Barbie dolls." TOM FENTON AND MARY HEFFRON (TFMH)

Back to Kampuchea. Produced by Martin Duckworth. 1982. 57 minutes. Color film and video. First Run Features. Rental: $100 (film only). Purchase: $850 (film), $500 (video). Also from IDERA (Vancouver, B.C.).

"Martin Duckworth's *Back to Kampuchea* documents the difficult but determined struggle of the people of Kampuchea (formerly Cambodia) to rebuild their country after the tragic destruction of the Vietnam War and the despotic rule of the Khmer Rouge. The film reveals to Westerners, for the first time, the efforts of over 5 million Khmer people to re-establish their ancient culture and create a new socialist society using the Vietnamese model.

"The film shows the story of a contemporary Kampuchea through the eyes of a Khmer taxi driver living in New York City, Chan Bun Han, who wished to return to his native land to search for family and friends. Through his encounters with survivors, he gathers some of the threads of his people's unfortunate history including the American bombing of the land and the massive genocide under the authoritarian regime of Pol Pot.

"The hopeful new outlook of the Khmer people is illustrated through Chan's visits to a primary school, a pagoda, and a public elections meeting. *Back To Kampuchea* creates a compassionate portrait of the revitalization of a nation." DISTRIBUTOR (DIST)

The Bases of Our Fears. Produced by Mennonite Central Committee Information Services. Written and narrated by Pat Hostetter Martin. Photography by Blair Seitz. 1983. Color slideshow or filmstrip with cassette tape and script. Mennonite Central Committee (Akron, Pa.). Rental: free. Purchase: $50 (slideshow), $15 (filmstip). Also from the Philippine Resource Center (Berkeley, Calif.)

MCC church-worker Pat Hostetter Martin speaks in a very personal manner about the fears and insecurities that lead governments to demand an increase in weaponry and about U.S. military bases in the Philippines. She critically examines the reasons given for the bases and then leads the audience on a tour of the town of Olongapo, adjacent to the U.S. naval base at Subic Bay, introducing the women whose only means of support is entertaining U.S. personnel. Filipinos like Sr. Mary John Mananzan and Senator José Diokno speak critically about the bases as invitations to nuclear attack in the event of hostilities.

Church audiences will find this presentation especially suitable, but it is appropriate for other groups as well. TFMH

Bayan Ko: Philippine Diary. Produced by Ilan Ziv of Tamouz Productions. 1984. 28 minutes. Color film or videotape (VHS). Maryknoll World Films. Rental: $25. Purchase: $350 (film).

"This documentary examines the dramatic struggles of four groups of marginated people in the Philippines who seek a more dignified life. The challenges they face are illustrated through the eyes of church workers who have chosen to share their destiny.

"The film opens with popular Filipino folk singer, Freddie Aguilar, in concert. His song, 'Bayan Ko,' which means 'my people,' expresses the longing of many for freedom and justice. The film goes on to show an Irish missioner in a Philippine jail. The priest was arrested for organizing landless peasants. Then residents of a Manila slum are seen joining a Filipina Sister in rallying middle-class women for social change. Next, drug addicts and prostitutes near Subic Bay Military Base are shown a way out by an Irish missioner. Finally, an American Maryknoll missioner in a

Mindanao slum dramatizes the new social role religion plays in Third World countries, such as the Philippines." DIST

Belau: The Price of Independence. Produced by Michel Bongiovani and Dasha Ross. 1984. 28 minutes. Color video (one-half inch VHS). U.S. Pacific Issues Network. Rental: $25.

"The Republic of Belau is today facing dramatic social, political, and cultural problems. This made-for-television video documentary examines for the first time the Pacific peoples' answers to the massive militarization of their region. Have the Belauns any other economic alternatives than to accept the offers of the U.S. government? Can this profoundly non-violent people stand up against the demands of the U.S. government?" DIST

Breaking Ground for Freedom. Produced and directed by Steven Carscallen and Patricia Youzwa. Edited by Christine Duval. 1984. 23 minutes. Color film. PIC (Montreal, Quebec). International sound track available. Rental: $50, plus postage. Purchase: $275 (film), $75 (video). Also from Philippine Resource Center (Berkeley, Calif.).

"*Breaking Ground* is the first documentary film on the social revolution underway in the Philippine countryside. Filmed inside guerrilla zones in southern Luzon, this film portrays the struggle of poor farmers to end centuries of poverty and to build an alternative society. Through interviews and shots of daily life, *Breaking Ground* shows the situation of coconut farmers living in two villages in the mountains and peasants organizing to solve the land question and improve their livelihood through cooperative agriculture.

"*Breaking Ground for Freedom* shows the role played by the New People's Army in mobilizing and assisting the farmers. Interviews with NPA fighters probe why these peasants, students, workers, and church people decided to join the liberation movement in the countryside." DIST

The Buddha Is Smiling: Nuclear Proliferation in Asia. Produced by Michael Bedford. 1983. 23 minutes. Center for Development Policy (Washington, D.C.). Rental: $20. Purchase: $65. Also from Committee for a New Korea Policy (Albany, N.Y.) and American Friends Service Committee (Cambridge, Mass.).

"This slideshow explores U.S. nuclear export policies which lead to unsafe reactors and corresponding risks of nuclear proliferation. Exposes U.S. complicity in the spread of nuclear technology (with little regard to health and safety considerations) in India, Pakistan, Taiwan, South Korea, and the Philippines." AFSC

The Business of Hunger. Produced by Robert Richter. 1985. 28 minutes. Color film or videotape (VHS). Maryknoll World Films. Rental: $25. Purchase: $325 (film).

"Award-winning producer Robert Richter examines one cause of hunger in Africa and throughout the world: agribusiness. *The Business of Hunger* shows how multinational corporations acquire land in underdeveloped countries and grow export crops. This results in small farmers losing their land. These displaced persons exacerbate the hunger problem since they become migrant workers on plantations or slum dwellers in the cities. Also, the amount of food available in the homeland is reduced.

"This 28-minute documentary illustrates this situation in the Philippines, Senegal, Brazil, and the Dominican Republic. It shows the harvests of these new corporate estates—pineapples, peanuts, and sugar—en route to the factories and tables of wealthy nations. The film offers hopeful alternatives and shows American citizens attempting to change the situation through creation of consumer cooperatives and the lobbying of congress members." DIST

Cambodia: Year One. Directed by John Pilger. 1980. 60 minutes. Color film. American Friends Service Committee (Cambridge, Mass.). Rental: $25. Also in video cassette from IDERA (Vancouver, B.C.).

"Another unique film for British TV by journalist John Pilger, *Year One* portrays one of the greatest success stories in history: Kampuchea pulls back from the brink of famine and cultural annihilation and begins the process of recovery and reconstruction.

"The film contrasts the stark horror of the Kampuchea left by Pol Pot [as shown in the film *Year Zero*, see below] with the vibrancy of a nation and people determined to put their country back together. Highlights the great contributions made by Vietnam, the Soviet Union, Oxfam, and the international agencies. Focuses also on the dangers to recovery posed by China's and the United States' continued support for the Pol Pot Khmer Rouge regime.

"Fascinating footage from the Thai refugee camps. Enlightening interview with a Khmer Rouge commander and proof of diversion of Western food aid to the Pol Pot soldiers. Excellent for countering Western propaganda about Vietnam's aims in Kampuchea." DIST

Cambodia: Year Zero. 1979. 60 minutes. Color film. American Friends Service Committee (Cambridge, Mass.). Rental: $25. Also in video cassette from IDERA (Vancouver, B.C.).

"The incredible story of Cambodia from 1975 to 1979. The brutality of the Pol Pot years is starkly portrayed, but is placed within a sound historical and political context. The need for international aid and the politics underlying the food aid controversy are emphasized. A must for anyone trying to understand the new crisis in Indochina." DIST

Celso and Cora. Produced, directed, photographed, and edited by Gary Kildea. Local collaboration by Rowena Katalingkasan. Produced with the participation of the Australian Film Commission, the Institute of Philippine Culture (Ateneo University, Manila), and NAV Productions (Tokyo). 1983. 109 minutes. Color film. Icarus Films. Rental: $125, plus postage. Purchase: $1,250 (film), $890 (video). Rental is for 3 days. In Tagalog with English subtitles. Also from the Philippine Resource Center (Berkeley, Calif.).

"Australian independent filmmaker Gary Kildea has produced this feature-length 'direct-cinema' film about a young couple and their two children living in Manila. They make a living selling cigarettes on the sidewalk outside a downtown hotel. These are poor people, but the film deals as much in individual psychology and the universal politics of family life as it does with this particular family's everyday efforts, against all odds, to keep feeding their children.

"The story of their lives over a three-month period is constructed, without commentary, from a compilation of detail, episode by episode, like the exposition of a dramatic narrative. *Celso and Cora* relies on 'to-camera' conversation and on observed interactional discussion among the main characters, their extended family members, and the other people they come in contact with daily." DIST

Chained Hands in Prayer. 1977. 30 minutes. Color slideshow with cassette tape. American Friends Service Committee (Cambridge, Mass.). Rental: $15. Also for sale ($100) from Pacific-Asia Resource Center (Tokyo).

"An audiovisual composition based on political prisoner Kim Chi Ha's poems. Kim Chi Ha was jailed by the U.S.-backed South Korean dictatorship of General Park Chung Hee because of Kim's undaunted critical spirit and hatred for injustice and tyranny. Kim's words, full of love and agony, are an appeal for solidarity with the Korean people who have suffered too long under the heel of South Korean dictatorships and they are an inspiration to people seeking liberation around the world." DIST

CIA Case Officer. Produced by the Institute for Policy Studies. 1978. 30 minutes. Color film and video. New Time Films. Rental: $50 (film). Purchase: $500 (film), $375 (video).

"John 'Bob' Stockwell, a CIA agent for twelve years, grew up in the Congo, the son of missionaries. In an in-depth character portrait, we meet a complex individual who asks important questions about patriotism, morality, and professionalism. Stockwell, who served the CIA mostly in Africa and Vietnam, talks with candor and introspection about his career and the disillusionment that led to his resignation in 1976." DIST

Collision Course. Produced by British Broadcasting Company. 1979. 40 minutes. Color film. American Friends Service Committee (Cambridge, Mass). Rental: $20. Also from Mennonite Central Committee (Akron, Pa.).

"The BBC's searing analysis of human rights violations in the Philippines—including the use of torture. Dramatic interviews with political dissidents, religious leaders, and government officials expose the hypocrisy and brutality of the Marcos regime. Connects human rights violations to economic conditions. *Collision Course* provides an excellent case study of political repression under a U.S.-supported dictatorship. A must for those interested in the human rights issue. Particularly good for religious and church groups as it shows the Philippine church in opposition to the Marcos government." DIST

The Corporate Connection. Produced by Committee for a New Korea Policy. 1984. 20 minutes. Color slideshow with cassette tape and script. Committee for a New Korea Policy. Rental: $15. Purchase: $65. Postage extra on rental.

"*Corporate Connection* examines:(1) corporations that leave American cities in search of low-paid labor; (2) grain companies that work to change Korean dietary habits; (3) computer firms that make South Korea's pass card system possible; (4) the relationship between U.S. support for a repressive government in South Korea and that government's help to U.S.

multinationals; (5) U.S. policies that encourage corporations to set up overseas.

"This slideshow is recommended for church and community groups, as well as college and high school classes." DIST

Developmental Aid: Like It or Not. 1983. 25 minutes. Color slideshow with cassette tape. 60 color slides with script. Synapses. Rental: $15. Rental is for 10 days.

"This slideshow looks into government-to-government developmental aid programs, in this case the Australia-Philippines road building and agricultural program in Mindanao.

"*Developmental Aid* has these objectives: (1) to show the effect of top-down development programs; (2) to challenge Western viewers' frame of reference that underdeveloped countries need to be led; and (3) to experience how media can be used for propaganda.

"The producers of this slideshow hope that the audience [will] become convinced that there are two sides to all positions and hence [will] critically analyze all such similar development programs and all media reports." DIST

Ecocide: A Strategy of War. Produced by E.W. Pfeiffer and Green Mountain Post Films. 1981. 23 minutes. Color film. Green Mountain Post Films. Rental: $45. Purchase: $400 (film), $225 (videotape). Study guide available.

"During the Vietnam War, the United States made massive use of chemicals and other means to destroy the cover and food sources used by the National Liberation Front.

"Between 1969 and 1973, Dr. E.W. Pfeiffer, a University of Montana zoologist and an outspoken critic of these tactics, made five trips to Indochina to study and document the ecological effects of the war. This award-winning film (re-edited and released in 1981) is the result of his study of chemical defoliation, bombing, and plowing of forests on a massive scale.

"*Ecocide* vividly documents the effects of these unprecedented tactics and shows some of the efforts by the people of Vietnam to rebuild their land. The film forcefully brings home the threat which a war strategy aimed at the ecology poses, not only for its direct victims, but also for the rest of humanity." DIST

See also: *The Secret Agent* and *War Shadows,* both from Green Mountain Post Films.

Front Line: A New Look at the Vietnam War. Produced and directed by David Bradbury. 1980. 55 minutes. Color film. Filmmaker's Library. Rental: inquire. Purchase: $800 (film), $650 (videotape).

"The focus of this Academy Award nominee documentary is Neil Davis, a courageous, humane news-cameraman who spent eleven years in the combat zone. His close-up footage combined with his recollections are a testimony to the horrors of war."

[Neil Davis was killed in the line of duty during an abortive coup attempt in Thailand in September 1985.]

"As an Australian, Davis viewed the conflict from a different perspective than an American. He spent much time with the Vietnamese troops, forming a deep attachment to the brave soldiers he lived among. Thus, *Front Line* shows a story, little known in the United States, of Asians suffering at the hands of other Asians. Davis was even permitted to cross enemy lines and film the other side of the war. And he was the only Western journalist to film the fall of Saigon.

"When *Front Line* was telecast nationally on PBS, the public interest was overwhelming. Americans who remembered those times gained new insight on the war. Younger audiences could see why Vietnam was such a divisive part of American history." DIST

Generations: A Chinese Family. 1984. 28 minutes. Color film. Maryknoll World Films. Rental: $25. Purchase: $350.

"*Generations* is about a four-generation family in the north China village of Long Bow. Doctor Shen Fasheng is a traditional Chinese doctor. He introduces us to his wife, grandmother, children, and grandchildren. Together they relate their family history and share with the viewer an intimate glimpse of their daily lives. We accompany them to work, to school, in prayer, at a funeral, and at a wedding.

"This documentary is a warm and unforgettable portrait of a contemporary Chinese family as they embrace traditions and meet new challenges. Both entertaining and instructive, this film is an excellent introduction to China for schools, study groups, civic, and social organizations." DIST

The Gentle People: A Look inside Laos. Produced by Jacqui Chagnon and Roger Rumpf. 1982. 24 minutes. Color slideshow with cassette tape, accented with Lao music. 140 slides. Asia Resource Center. Rental: $25. Purchase: $55.00 ($45.00 for refugee groups only). Note: the producers are available for speaking engagements to accompany presentations of *The Gentle People.* Also from American Friends Service Committee (Cambridge, Mass.) and from Mennonite Central Committee (Akron, Pa. and Winnipeg, Manitoba).

"An introduction to the people, culture, and post-war conditions of Laos. A look at everyday life that highlights the similarities and differences among Laos's sixty ethnic groups, including the Hmong, Lao, Mien, and Thai Dam people. Examines the mental and physical scars left by thirty years of war and the struggle for survival of one of the poorest countries in the world.

"Excellent for groups of Lao refugees and their sponsors. Helpful for school, church, and community groups in building a cross-cultural bridge." AFSC

Hearts and Minds. Produced by Peter Davis and Bert Schneider. 1975. 90 minutes. Color film. American Friends Service Committee (Cambridge, Mass.). Inquire for rates.

"Academy Award-winning documentary on the Vietnam War and the roots of the war in the American consciousness and American institutions. Best film available on the true nature of the war, its background, its conduct, and its impact on the lives of Vietnamese and Americans.

"Interviews with Dan Ellsberg, General Westmoreland, Walt Rostow, and others sharpen the debate. Excellent section on the role racism played in the U.S. conduct of the war.

"Best educational tool available to counter present-day attempts to rewrite the history of the war. It also helps correct the gross distortions of the war portrayed in films like *Deerslayer* and *Apocalypse Now*." DIST

How Yukong Moved the Mountains. Produced by Joris Ivens and Marcelline Loridan. 1977. 720 minutes. Color film. 12-parts. Cinema Arts Association. Rental: $35. Rental cost ranges up to $125.

This series of twelve films by two outstanding documentary filmmakers covers nearly every aspect of people's lives in modern China. Topics range from women to an army camp, from factories to an experimental pharmacy. TFMH

Human Rights and Social-Economic Conditions in Indonesia, West Papua, and East Timor. Produced by TAPOL-UK. 1984. Color and black and white slideshow with script. 70 slides. TAPOL-UK. Rental: inquire for rates. Purchase: £25.00 for institutes and libraries; £12.50 for individuals and solidarity groups. Postage extra.

"This slideshow consists of five parts: (1) introduction and the power of the military; (2) Indonesia's economy and the society in rural and urban areas; (3) human rights violations and repression in Indonesia; (4) Indonesia's war against East Timor; and (5) Indonesian rule in West Papua and West Papuan resistance." DIST

India: Myths and Realities. Produced by Manji Pendakur. 1978. 15 minutes. Color filmstrip. IDERA. Rental: inquire for rates.

"The myth of India as a fatalistic society is exploded in this filmstrip production that contrasts the Western image of India with the reality of the many Indians who are working to build a better society. It explores the legacy of two centuries of British colonial rule, looks at the nature of development that has taken place in the last thirty years, and attempts to answer such questions as: Has foreign aid helped the Indian people at large? Who enjoys the benefits from modern industry? Why is there still such massive starvation?" DIST

Inside North Korea. Produced by Committee for a New Korea Policy. 1981. 20 minutes. Color slideshow with cassette tape. 99 slides. Committee for a New Korea Policy. Rental: $15. Purchase: $75. Postage extra on rental.

"Based on the visit of an American Quaker delegation in 1980, *Inside North Korea* attempts to answer two questions: What is life like in North Korea? And, how should the United States relate to this country?

"Both positive and negative aspects of North Korean society are discussed. There are pictures of homes, schools, factories, and farms." DIST

Korea: Time for a Change. Produced by Maud Easter and David Easter for the American Friends Service Committee. 1981. 25 minutes. Color slideshow with cassette tape. American Friends Service Committee (Cambridge, Mass.). Rental: $15. Purchase: $50. Filmstrip with tape available for sale: $40.

"A look at daily life in North and South Korea and the impact of U.S. policy on this divided peninsula. Examines developments in the North and South that will have an effect on the area's future. Considers how militarization of the peninsula threatens peace. Looks at how U.S. power and presence in the South and U.S. policy toward the North is affecting the Koreans, and suggests other choices for U.S. policy makers." DIST

Looking for China: American Images (Part 1). Produced by Asia Society, China Council. 1980. 18 minutes. Color slideshow with cassette tape. Asia Society, China Council. Purchase: $10.

Looking for America: Chinese Images (Part 2). Produced by Asia Society, China Council. 1980. 18 minutes. Color slideshow with cassette tape. Asia Society, China Council. Purchase: $10.

This two-part slideshow presents images people in China and the U.S. have of each other based on newspaper cartoons, magazines, movies, and other sources. TFMH

See also: *Misunderstanding China,* a fifty-four minute color documentary first televised on the eve of President Nixon's first visit to China. Using clips from old Hollywood films and comic books, this film tries to get viewers to reassess their stereotypes of China and the Chinese people. *Misunderstanding China* is available from the four regional offices of the US-China People's Friendship Association for a rental fee of $20 (groups) or $35 (institutions).

Marshall Islands: America's Radioactive "Trust." Produced by Micronesia Support Committee. 1980. 25 minutes. Color slideshow with script. 120 slides. Pacific Concerns Resource Center. Purchase: $75.00 for individuals and non-profit organizations; $100 for institutions.

"This set of slides focuses on the devastating health and environmental effects of the United States' sixty-six atomic and hydrogen bomb tests in the Marshall Islands. Details the forced resettlement of the Bikini and Eniwetak people, the radiation exposure to Marshallese and American service personnel and resulting health problems, and attempts to clean up and re-inhabit the former nuclear test sites of Bikini and Eniwetak." DIST

Micronesia: America's Strategic Islands. Micronesia Support Committee. 1983. Color slideshow. 129 slides. Pacific Concerns Resource Center. Purchase: $75 for individuals and nonprofit groups; $100 for institutions.

"This slideshow features an overview of Micronesia since World War II, focusing on the nuclear tests in the Marshalls, the Kwajalein Missile Range, future political status of the islands, U.S. policies creating economic dependency, future military plans for the Marianas, Belau, and other islands, and peoples' movements to determine their own future."DIST

Nuclear Free Pacific. 1984. 30 minutes. Color slideshow with script. 140 slides. U.S. Pacific Issues Network. Rental: $20. Purchase: $100.

"This half-hour presentation introduces the global arms race and then focuses on the unique legacy and present role of the Pacific region. The peoples and lands of the Pacific are briefly introduced and their history of nuclear and military exploitation is told.

"The U.S. role in Micronesia, the testing in the Marshall Islands, the Kwajalein Missile Range, and the Nuclear-Free Constitution struggle in Belau are all discussed. Brief mention is also made of the other anti-nuclear and self-determination issues in the Pacific. An excellent primer." DIST

People of the Field. 1981. 14 minutes. Color slideshow with cassette tape and script. 80 slides. Synapses. Rental: $15. Rental is for 10 days.

"A general introduction to the situation and struggle of rural and urban poor in the Philippines and how the people of North America are connected to that struggle." DIST

People of the Field is addressed to a religious audience, but secular audiences will not find the religious emphasis intrusive. The slideshow explains the role of handicrafts in the lives of the poor and of political prisoners and encourages their purchase by people in North America. TFMH

Phantom India. Directed by Louis Malle. 1967–68. 364 minutes. Color film. Seven 52-minute parts. New Yorker Films. Rental: $700. Rental is for entire series if shown in 2-week period.

"*Phantom India* does justice to its almost overwhelming subject: the totality of India. One of the most ambitious films ever attempted, Louis Malle's documentary takes the viewer on an epic journey, crammed with sights and insights on not only mainstream topics like the caste system, religious thought, the cities, poverty and the impact of modernism, but also the edges which illuminate the whole—the movie industry, a dancing school, a birth control clinic, a red light district, strange tribes, esoteric cults, and exotic locales. Malle's attitude toward his material is the cinematic opposite of imperialism: never dogmatic, filled with humility and wonder." DIST

Individual 52-minute episodes of *Phantom India* are available for a rental fee of $150 each. The episodes are:

1. *The Impossible Camera.* Daily life of Indian fishers and peasants, the temple of Konarak, the contradictions of hunger and the beauty of the surrounding nature, women constructing an immense tourist hotel brick by brick.
2. *Things Seen in Madras.* The south of India, the Dravidian culture, a movie studio, a traditional dancing school.
3. *The Indians and the Sacred.* Asceticism, sadhus wandering along the roads, the ashrams, Hinduism as a negation of earthly being.
4. *Dream and Reality.* Kerala, a state of great natural beauty with the highest percentage of literacy and the first state in the union to have a communist majority. Tea plantations, fishing villages, and palm forests.
5. *Look at the Castes.* The caste system in a village of Rajastan—its organization, social hierarchy, and economic activity.
6. *On the Fringes of Indian Society.* The Bondo, Jews, Catholics, Pondicherry Ashram, Toda tribe and other groups living in India that have not integrated into its society.
7. *Bombay—The Future India.* City of five million inhabitants—six hundred thousand living in the streets—with its stock exchange, slums, political demonstrations, and economic boom. TFMH

Pinugngang Agus. 1984. 20 minutes. Color slideshow with cassette tape and script. Synapses. Purchase: $50.

"*Pinugngang Agus* examines human rights abuses in the Philippines and the church's response to them. The slideshow probes the economic reasons for the use of military force to protect corporate interests, presenting solid data with artistic style." DIST

Politics of Torture. Produced by "ABC-Close-Up." 1978. 50 minutes. Color film. California Newsreel. Rental: $50. Purchase: $650.

This film exposes evidence of brutal repression by the Philippine government and other U.S. allies and raises questions about U.S. government and private support for such regimes. It documents examples of repression in Iran and Chile as well as the Philippines. TFMH

Prisoners of Conscience. Directed by Anand Patwardhan. 1978. 45 minutes. Black and white film. Icarus Films. Rental: $60.

During the state of emergency imposed on India (June 1975 to March 1977) by the late Indira Gandhi, more than one hundred thousand people were arrested without charge and imprisoned without trial. *Prisoners of Conscience* examines the situation of political prisoners in India during and prior to the emergency. TFMH

Public Enemy No. 1: A Radical Journalist in War-Torn Asia. Produced and directed by David Bradbury. 1981. 55 minutes. Color film. Filmmaker's Library. Rental: $80. Purchase: $800 (film), $650 (videotape).

"Australian journalist Wilfred Burchett was radicalized at Hiroshima where he was the first Western journalist to witness the devastation. Disillusioned with the West, Burchett reported the Korean and Vietnam wars from the communist side. In his home country he was considered a traitor and exiled.

"In *Public Enemy No. 1* Burchett is filmed returning to Asia in his seventies to confront his past. He is horrified by the carnage in Cambodia of the Pol Pot regime, which he had championed. Had his loyalty been misplaced?

"This fascinating award-winning documentary, interwoven with archival footage, raises serious questions about journalistic freedom and responsibility." DIST

Report from Kwangju. 1980. 30 minutes. Color film. American Friends Service Committee (Cambridge, Mass.). Rental: $25.

"Never before released footage of the dramatic worker-student takeover of the city of Kwangju, South Korea—a key event in the Korean human rights movement in the aftermath of the assassination of General Park Chung Hee. Taken by U.S. television crews, this film shows the violent crushing of the uprising by South Korean army units. This footage was censored out of U.S. evening news. Given the role the U.S. plays in South Korea, an understanding of this democratic uprising in a major South Korean city is crucial." DIST

Reports from Iran and Afghanistan. Produced by Jon Alpert. 1980. 30 minutes. Color videotape (VHS and Beta). Downtown Community Television Center (DCTV). Rental: $30. Purchase: $90.

During the holding of the American hostages at the U.S. Embassy in Tehran, DCTV traveled throughout Iran to learn something about the Iranian people and to provide background on the country's urban and rural conditions.

"In addition," DCTV writes, "we walked across the border to Afghanistan and became the first American reporters to witness the fighting inside

Afghanistan. Traveling with a rebel unit that was fighting in the desert we were able to capture a revealing picture of the Afghani rebels." TFMH

Risks and Benefits. Produced by Peter Heller. 1978. 30 minutes. Color film. IDERA. Rental: $40.

"This West German film looks at the social and economic impact of a large high-rise housing development built by a German multinational corporation in Penang, Malaysia. Originally designed as a low-income housing development, the complex soon became an expensive vertical slum and is a classic example of how multinationals succeed in imposing costly, inappropriate development on Third World countries." DIST

Rough Road to Recovery. 1980. 23 minutes. Color slideshow with script. American Friends Service Committee (Cambridge, Mass.). Rental: $15.

"Based on an American Friends Service Committee tour of Cambodia in early 1980, this slideshow presents more updated information on food aid to Cambodia, attempts at reconstruction, and the political situation in the country." DIST

Sangham: Aid to Liberation. Produced by Peter Krieg and Heidi Knott. 1978. 30 minutes. Color film. IDERA. Rental: $40.

"As the most suppressed and downtrodden group among India's poor, the Harijans or untouchables in India's caste system have to lie outside the village, drink water from separate wells, and sit aside when the village council meets. Their protests have been met with stiff resistance and sometimes violence.

"This is today's reality in many parts of rural India. But several villages near Hyderabad in Andhra Prodesh are giving birth to something new. Guided and helped by a small group of Indian social workers, the Harijans are organizing themselves into village unions *(sanghams)* and are forming their own production cooperatives and night schools.

"This West German documentary records this process and effectively illustrates how development aid can be used to help people towards their emancipation." DIST

Season of Thunder. Produced by Jeffrey Chester, Charles Drucker, Scott Robinson, Joel Rocamora, and Ismael Saavedra, 1983. 60 minutes. Color film. English narration. Spanish version also available. Philippine Resource Center. Rental: $75. Postage extra on rental. Purchase: $750, plus shipping. Also in video (VHF and Beta), $50.

"In the remote mountains of the northern Philippines, the traditional way of life of the Igorot people has been shattered by a bloody conflict with the Marcos government. *Season of Thunder* documents the struggle of these tribal Filipinos to preserve their culture and protect their land.

"Over centuries, the Igorot people have created a unique adaptation to the mountainous terrain, carving the slopes into magnificent tiers of rice terraces. Proposed dams along the Chico River, logging concessions in ancestral forests, mines, and other development projects, built or backed by the government, would destroy the mountain landscape and the Igorot culture.

"The Igorots' opposition to the expropriation of their lands has escalated into an open rebellion against the government and its troops. To strengthen their resistance, and to counter increased militarization in the countryside, the Igorots have joined a nationwide rebellion along with guerrillas of the New People's Army (NPA).

"With the help of the NPA, the Igorots forced the Marcos government to postpone construction of the Chico dams. Their success has been internationally heralded as an important victory for indigenous peoples' rights. *Season of Thunder* presents the story of this struggle through the eyes of a tribal Filipina. It is a powerful and sympathetic portrait of the Philippine resistance." DIST

Shallow Graves. 1982. 18 minutes. Color slideshow with cassette tape. Synapses. Rental: $15. Purchase: $50. 88 slides. Rental is for 10 days. Also from Mennonite Central Committee (Akron, Pa., and Calgary, Alberta).

"This slide set is a powerful and graphic documentary on the struggle for peace and justice of Christian communities on the Philippine island of Negros, where much military violence has occurred.

"Some of the citizens who work for peace in these communities have mysteriously disappeared; their bodies were later found in shallow graves. Many villagers live in fear of their lives, others flee to the lowlands in search of safety, leaving their ready-to-be-harvested rice crops behind." DIST

Southeast Asia Report: Cambodia, Vietnam, China. 2 parts. Produced by Downtown Community Television Center. 1975. 30 minutes. Color film. Downtown Community Television Center. (DCTV). Rental: $30. Purchase: $100. Data applies to each of 2 parts.

"The Vietnam War ended in 1975, but Southeast Asia has never recovered and peace is still elusive. In an exclusive series of reports DCTV traces events in this suffering region. It is a story of war—the initial border clashes between China and Vietnam—as China attempted to punish its former ally for invading Cambodia, and of genocide as the horrors of life under Pol Pot are revealed to the camera.

"DCTV was the first Western TV crew to enter Cambodia after the overthrow of Pol Pot. Death, destruction, and starvation were everywhere. Families were wiped out, the cities emptied, the fields left dry and bare. These reports show the tragedies and pain of a war-torn people in the effort to rebuild their country. Through personal stories we experience the suffering of the Cambodian people as well as their pride and tremendous will to survive.

"Part 1: An examination of the first border conflicts between Vietnam and Cambodia, including footage from the border and an analysis of the situation by journalists, scholars, and U.S. State Department officials.

"Part 2: A series of news reports covering the war between China and Vietnam, the Vietnamese occupation of Cambodia, and the carnage left by the Pol Pot regime." DIST

Strategic Trust: The Making of Nuclear-Free Palau. Directed by James Heddle. 1984. 59 minutes. Color film. Cinema Guild. Rental: $100. Purchase: $895 (film), $750 (video).

"This award-winning documentary tells the timely and dramatic story of Palau, an emerging island republic in America's Pacific Trust Territory, as it becomes history's first nuclear-free nation despite U.S. military plans to make it a nuclear weapons storage base. The film raises a key global issue, nuclear self-determination—whether local citizens have the right to decide if nuclear weapons will be deployed on their soil. The film also examines other issues such as the decolonization process, the politics of foreign aid, minority rights, and America's willingness to support its own transplanted democratic values." DIST

Television's Vietnam: The Impact of Visual Images. Produced by Peter Rollins and David Culbert. 1982. 180 minutes. Color film. Your Film Center. Rental: $60. Purchase: $1,500.

"*Television's Vietnam* is designed to prepare viewers to see critically and to raise their media consciousness so that they can weigh and evaluate the truthfulness and representativeness of what they see on TV. This film has multiple uses in the classroom: teachers of history and journalism can use the program to discuss the dependence of Americans on media; teachers of the arts—literature, photography, music—can use the program to examine the interpretive dimension of visual and aural media; finally, anyone specifically concerned with American consciousness in the 1960s or anyone treating the fiction and nonfiction related to the Vietnam experience will find this film useful.

"Interviews with government officials explore tensions within the Johnson White House. Military leaders at all levels—from General William Westmoreland to front line enlisted men—discuss the strategic and technical dimensions of controversial battles. The news community is represented by Pulitzer Prize–winning photographers, producers, and reporters. The person in the street comments upon the impact of visual images. Whenever possible veteran perceptions and experiences are contrasted with visual reports of the same events." DIST

Tenants in Our Own Land. Produced by Mennonite Missionaries. 1979. 22 minutes. Color slideshow with tape and script. 80 slides. Synapses. Purchase: $30.

An examination of Castle and Cooke's Dolefil and Standard Philippine Fruit (bananas and pineapples) operations in the southern Philippines. Told through four characters: the Philippine minister of economic development, a small banana grower, the president of Castle and Cooke, and a pineapple plantation worker. TFMH

There Was an Evening, There Was a Morning. 1975. 60 minutes. Color film. American Friends Service Committee (Cambridge, Mass.). Rental: $20.

"A film about the liberation of Vietnam, made by a group of Vietnamese Catholic clergy and laypeople in 1975 and distributed by the Communité Vietnamien, Paris. There are two half-hour reels. The first is a documentary and may be used by itself. The second is made up of interviews concerning the role of religious institutions in prewar and postwar Vietnam." DIST

They Will Never Forget. Produced by People's Film of Thailand (Bangkok) and Pacific-Asia Resource Center (Tokyo). 1977. 30 minutes. 8mm color film. Pacific-Asia Resource Center. Purchase: $350, airmail postage included.

This documentary of the takeover and collective operation of the Harah jeans factory in Bangkok by the plant's women workers is set against the background of Thailand's short-lived period of democracy in the mid-1970s. TFMH

This Bloody Blundering Business. Produced by Peter Davis. 1978. 30 minutes. Black and white film. Cinema Guild. Rental: $50. Purchase: $425 (film), $300 (video). Also from the American Friends Service Committee (Cambridge, Mass.) and from the Philippine Resource Center (Berkeley, Calif.).

"Uses archival footage to vividly portray the U.S. war of annexation against the Philippines in the late 1800s and early 1900s. An eye-opening experience that documents U.S. atrocities and the role played by racism in this all-out war against the entire civilian population. A must for those interested in understanding U.S. intervention in Vietnam in the 1950s, 1960s, and 1970s, and in Central America in 1984." AFSC

The United States in Vietnam: How Did It Happen? Produced by Indochina Curriculum Group. 1975. 20 minutes. Color filmstrip with cassette tape. Script includes notes, questions, and activity suggestions. American Friends Service Committee. Rental: $15. Also available from the Institute for Peace and Justice (St. Louis).

"The best short history available on how the United States got involved in Vietnam. An excellent educational tool to help counter the dangerously deceptive but appealing interpretations of the war being portrayed through films such as *The Deerhunter* and through the distortion by media and government of the boat people tragedy." DIST

Vietnam: An American Journey. Directed by Bob Richter. 1978. 90 minutes. Color film. American Friends Service Committee (Cambridge, Mass.). Inquire for rates. Also from Films Incorporated (Wilmette, Ill.).

"American filmmaker Robert Richter's seven-week trip down Highway 1, from Hanoi to Ho Chi Minh City (Saigon). An enlightening and touching portrait of civilian rehabilitation after and during a national trauma.

"Film critic Pat Augderheide writes: 'The film dramatically reminds us of what we have rarely understood: that real people lived at the other end of all those military fights. It shocks us that we are shocked by a peacetime Vietnam. . . .'

"*An American Journey* advocates, in a nonpolemical way, American reparations and international aid for Vietnam." DIST

Vietnam: A Television History. Produced by WGBH Boston. 1983. Color film. 13 one-hour segments. A package of transcripts of each of the thirteen programs is available for $44 from the producer: P.O. Box 322, Boston, MA 02134. Films Incorporated. Inquire for rates.

Six years in the making, this documentary series premiered on public television in the fall of 1983. *Vietnam: A Television History* is unquestionably the most comprehensive film exploration ever made of the background and history of the war in Vietnam.

The program's producers advertise a range of educational materials that "were developed to help viewers assimilate the experience of Vietnam while supporting a rigorous examination of the historical and political context of the period." The educational materials were designed to support several types of use: (1) a course for credit, licensed by the Public Broadcasting System Adult Learning Service; (2) an educational supplement for classroom use; and (3) an important addition to library video reference collections and a facilitator for community discussion groups. TFMH

Send a self-addressed stamped envelope to Third World Resources, 464 19 St., Oakland, CA 94612 for a two-page descriptive guide to the educational materials that accompany *Vietnam: A Television History.*

Vietnam: Picking Up the Pieces. Produced by Downtown Community Television Center and WNET/TV. 1978. 60 minutes. Color film. Downtown Community Television Center (DCTV). Rental: $75. Purchase: $250. Color videotape reel-to-reel or cassette.

"In December 1977, DCTV made headlines around the country by becoming the first American television journalists allowed in Vietnam since the end of the fighting. For more than a month, with an unprecedented amount of access to the country's people, DCTV traveled throughout North and South Vietnam, now united under communist rule.

"In the South, people are trying to adjust to the new communist government, but many problems remain. The black market continues to thrive and there are more than one million unemployed. With food supplies running low, the government is trying desperately to shrink the overcrowded slums of Saigon by relocating people to the countryside. But millions of American mines are still buried beneath the soil. It will take years for the land to recover from the effects of combat.

"In the North, people still work to repair the damage from massive American air raids. Women construction crews work in Hanoi to rebuild schools, houses, and the badly bombed Bac Mai Hospital. The economy is badly shaken, with a surprising amount of private enterprise in operation." DIST

The Village of My An, 1881–1981. Produced by Center for Southeast Asian Studies, University of Michigan. 1981. 35 minutes. Color slideshow with cassette tape. 156 slides. Center for Southeast Asian Studies, University of Michigan. Purchase: $85. Available for rent from American Friends Service Committee (Cambridge, Mass.).

"*The Village of My An* traces the life of a peasant community in Vietnam over the last hundred years of social and political upheaval in that country. The breakdown of the traditional order under French colonial rule, the August Revolution of 1945, and the devastation brought about by American military intervention in Vietnam are presented as they affected a large segment of the rural population.

"The intent of both the narrative and the slides is to portray the villagers' way of life, the reasoning behind their political choices, and the resilience which sustained them through the last three decades of hardship and conflict.

"Although My An is not an actual village, it is a representative depiction of a Vietnamese rural community constructed from historical and ethnographic accounts of village life. The events related in this account are based entirely on the historical record." CSAS

Villages of Sorrow: The Story of Tribal Filipinos. Produced by Tribal Filipino Project. 1984. 27 minutes. Color slideshow with cassette tape and script. 250 slides. Philippine Resource Center. Rental: $25. Rental is for 3 days. Purchase with carousel: $350 (individuals), $450 (institutions).

"*Villages of Sorrow* is about tribal Filipinos, the impact of development on their traditional way of life, and their struggles to cope with dramatic social and economic changes throughout the Philippines. From the Mangyans living in the mountains of Mindoro to the Igorots of northern Luzon, tribal Filipinos are the victims of corporate developers and their protectors—the military. Today, tribes throughout the Philippines are experiencing loss of their traditional homelands and quality of life, and in many cases are faced with the threat of their destruction as a distinct people.

"With backing from the United States and the World Bank, the Philippine government is financing development of dams which threaten to flood the traditional homelands of the Igorot tribe. U.S. military bases in central Luzon have already destroyed the homelands of the Negrito tribe. Foreign investment in logging and agribusiness is destroying the traditional homelands of tribes throughout the Philippines.

"The Philippine government created its own agency (PANAMIN) to facilitate the integration of tribes into the market economy. The military has forced tribes that have resisted loss of their land into strategic hamlets designed to prevent them from making contact with the New People's Army (NPA).

"Many of the tribes, however, have joined the ranks of the twenty thousand NPA troops. *Villages of Sorrow* shows how tribal Filipinos are joining forces with other Filipinos to fight for their freedom and human dignity." DIST

When the Almsgiving Stops. 1980. 22 minutes. Color slideshow with cassette tape. American Friends Service Committee (Cambridge, Mass.). Rental: $20.

"Best program to use as an introduction to the issues of world hunger and overpopulation. Using Bangladesh and its poverty, overpopulation, and hunger as a case study, this slide program gets to the real causes of hunger—and finds them in distribution of wealth, land ownership, and land-use patterns.

"*When the Almsgiving Stops* helps people see that distribution of economic and political power is the key issue to address in order to end hunger. Good analogies to the U.S. food system." DIST

Where Will We Hang the Lightbulbs? Produced by Gene Stoltzfus and Dorothy Friesen. 1979. 15 minutes. Color slideshow with cassette tape. Mennonite Central Committee (Akron, Pa., and Kitchener, Ontario). Free. Available for rent from American Friends Service Committee (Cambridge, Mass.) and for half-price purchase ($30) from Synapses (Chicago, Ill.).

"A very beautiful and powerful slideshow on the conflict between ancient cultures and corporate industrial development in Third World countries. The T'Boli are an ancient Philippine tribal group whose way of life is threatened by a hydroelectric project forced on them by the Marcos dictatorship. In the exchange between the T'Boli and the government, basic questions are raised about the place of human needs in the priorities behind economic development. Simple and clear." AFSC

Who Owns the Sky? 1978. 23 minutes. Color slideshow with cassette tape. American Friends Service Committee (Cambridge, Mass.). Rental: $15.

"A crystal-clear presentation of how large companies from developed countries take advantage of the political weakness of the people of Third World countries to expand their power. *Who Owns the Sky?* focuses on the Kawasaki Steel Corporation of Japan, showing how the pollution from one of its plants in one Japanese city was killing the population and ruining the city. In response to citizens' demands that it eliminate the pollution, Kawasaki moved the most polluting part of its operations to the Philippines where it disrupts the lives of thousands. There Kawasaki works hand-in-glove with the Marcos dictatorship.

"Shows clearly the economic function of authoritarian governments in Southeast Asia. Closes on a hopeful note showing the opposition throughout Asia to the irresponsibility toward the environment and human life by the big multinationals." DIST

Women in Korea. Produced by Committee for a New Korea Policy. 1984. 15 minutes. Color slideshow with cassette tape. 68 color slides. Committee for a New Korea Policy. Rental: $15. Purchase: $65. Postage extra on rental.

"*Women in Korea* describes the life of women in both South and North Korea, comparing and contrasting the social services of each society and showing women's struggle for equality, the impact of repressive governments, and the threat to women of U.S.-encouraged militarization." DIST

Women in Vietnam. 1980. 59 minutes. Color slideshow with script. American Friends Service Committee (Cambridge, Mass.). Rental: $15.

"Best educational tool available portraying the history of the development of the resistance movement in Vietnam and the critical role played by women in that movement. Spanning the centuries from the first Vietnamese independence war in the first century through 1975, *Women in Vietnam* focuses on the degradation of Vietnamese society—women in particular—under French Colonialism and during American occupation and on the developing resistance to that degradation.

"An excellent section on how the Western 'male' values held by foreign troops in Vietnam led to the dehumanization of women brings the war home to American women. This slideshow tells a story about Vietnam that few Americans get to hear." DIST

SUPPLEMENTARY LIST OF VISUAL RESOURCES

GENERAL ASIA AND PACIFIC

The Fly and the Axe. Color film. South Pacific Peoples Foundation of Canada.

No Road over Iriri Land. Color slideshow with cassette tape. South Pacific Peoples Foundation of Canada.

Trade Off in the Pacific. Color film. South Pacific Peoples Foundation of Canada.

Yumi Yet. Color film. 1975. South Pacific Peoples Foundation of Canada.

EAST TIMOR

East Timor. Videocassette. Forthcoming 1986. Indonesia East Timor Program (Toronto).

East Timor and the Canadian Connection. Color slideshow with script. 1985. Indonesia East Timor Program (Toronto).

INDIA

No Promise for Tomorrow: Communities Respond to the Bhopal Tragedy. Videocassette. 1985. Available for rental or purchase from the Highlander Center, Route 3, P.O. Box 370, New Market, TN 37820 and from the Society for Participatory Research in Asia, 45 Sainik Farm, Khanpur, New Delhi 110062, India.

KOREA

Korea: The Front Line of Freedom? Color slideshow with cassette tape. Available from the North American Coalition for Human Rights in Korea.

Korean Women Workers. Color slideshow with cassette tape. AFSC Nationwide Women's Project, 1501 Cherry St., Philadelphia, PA 19102.

PHILIPPINES

Healthy Business Videocassette. 1981. IDERA.

A Matter of Taste. Videocassette. 1981. IDERA.

The Pacific Era. Color slideshow with cassette tape. 1981. IDERA.

Turumba. Color film. 1982. 94 minutes. Les Blank Flower Films, 10341 San Pablo Ave., El Cerrito, CA 94530.

The following color slideshows (with cassette tape and script) are available from Interim Media Productions, P.O. Box 177, Ozamis City, Philippines. All are in English; most are in Visayan as well. Purchase price is in U.S. dollars. Postage is extra.

Eviction. 86 slides. 15 minutes. $50.
Fed Up/Taga Liog Na. 78 slides. 17 minutes. $50.
Fruits of Toil. 130 slides. 25 minutes. $95.
Live-in Fear. 59 slides. 14 minutes. $35.
Mindanao: The Bleeding Land. 50 slides. 8 minutes. $40.
The Quickie/Walang Aray. 93 slides. 15 minutes. $55.
The Return. 75 slides. 9 minutes. $45.
Social Volcano. 139 slides. 29 minutes. $65.
The Struggle of Generations: An Economic History of Philippine Underdevelopment. 164 slides. 40 minutes. $100.
Sunog/Fire. 61 slides. 14 minutes. $40.
The Vanishing Earth. 85 slides. 15 minutes. $45.
When the Lava Flows. 64 slides. 14 minutes. $35.
Who Owns the Plains? 144 slides. 44 minutes. $75.

INFORMATION SOURCES

For information on additional audiovisuals related to Asia and the Pacific consult the catalogs, directories, guides section above (pp. 37–38) and the curriculum guides and materials section below (pp. 108–112).

In addition, consult the catalogs of distributors represented in this directory, as well as these publications:

Audio-Visual Resources for Social Change. Cambride, Mass.: AFSC, 1981. Tabloid newspaper. 8pp. Free. Two supplements have been released: Winter 1982–Summer 1983 (2pp.) and 1984–85 (8pp.).

Audio-Visual Resources is an excellent guide for a number of reasons: it is an annotated list of over one hundred of the best audiovisuals available on social change; resources are classified under sixty-two headings, cross-referenced, and indexed; the catalog is kept up-to-date through periodic supplements; and—best of all—the audiovisuals listed in the catalogs are all available conveniently and inexpensively from the New England Regional Office of the American Friends Service Committee. Call to discuss rental procedures with AFSC's film librarian: (617) 497–5273.

Topical headings related to Asia and Pacific are: Bangladesh, Cambodia (Kampuchea), Indochina since 1975, the Indochina War, Japan, Korea, the Philippines, and Vietnam.

Educators Guide to Free Films. Comp. and ed. John C. Diffor and Elaine N. Diffor. Educators Progress Service, 214 Center St., Randolf, WI 53956. Annual.

The forty-fourth edition of this guide (1984) numbered 690 pages and included over 4,000 titles available in the United States and Canada.

Educators Guide to Free Filmstrips. Comp. and ed. John C. Diffor and Elaine N. Diffor. Educators Progress Service (address above). Annual.

The Thirty-sixth edition of this guide (1984) listed 438 titles in 148 pages.

Ethnic Film and Filmstrip Guide for Libraries and Media Centers. Ed. Lubomyr Wynar and Lois Buttar. Littleton, Colo.: Libraries Unlimited, 1980. Index.

Organized into sections covering over sixty ethnic groups, the entries in this directory include name, format (film or filmstrip), length, name of producer, date, audience level, and rental and sale prices.

Ethnic Information Sources of the United States. Ed. Paul Wasserman and Alice E. Kennington. 2 vols. Detroit: Gale Research, 1983. Index. See p. 39 above.

Each chapter in this book includes a list of audiovisual materials (maps, films, slideshows) with title, format, length, and source for each entry. Other sources for audiovisuals—usually the official information office of the nation involved—are included at the end of the list.

Films of China. 16mm Sound Films from and about the People's Republic of China. Washington, D.C.: USCPFA, December 1983. 8pp. Free.

This annotated list of audiovisuals about China covers the arts, culture, and sports; communes and factories; education; tourism; newsreels; health; national minorities; and other topics.

The listings for audiovisuals encompass feature-length films, animated shorts, slideshows, and filmstrips. Length, date, language, format, and the USCPFA distribution office to contact are given for each entry. USCPFA charges a minimal price for rental of the audiovisuals in this catalog: $20–35 for those less than sixty minutes, $30–60 for those longer than sixty minutes.

Filmstrips for Area Studies: A Critical Evaluation of K-12 Learning Materials. William Lipsky et al. Los Angeles: UCLA Graduate School of Education, Curriculum Inquiry Center, 1980. Occasional Paper no. 7. 290pp.

This guide devotes an entire section (pp. 208–67) to a critical review of thirty-four filmstrips on Asia and the Pacific. Audiovisuals are, however, limited to those produced from the early to the middle 1970s.

AUDIO RESOURCES: RECORDS, TAPES

ANNOTATED ENTRIES

Folkways Records, 632 Broadway, New York, NY 10012. Tel: (212)777-6606. Order numbers are given in parentheses for each of the records listed below.

Folkways has four series of 12-inch long-playing records that are relevant to the Asia and Pacific region: ethnic, history and documentary, international, and the spoken word.

Music in the *ethnic* and *international* series provides examples of folk and classical music from other cultures. These records could be used to set a mood for educational programs and to broaden the cultural awareness of students. Examples of the more than one hundred records in these categories are:

Music of Southeast Asia (4423),
Vocal Music of Contemporary China (4091 and 4092),
Folk Music of Pakistan (4425),
Ragas from South India (8854).

The *historical* records are didactic. The most notable Asia-related record in this category is:

Berkeley Teach-in: Vietnam. Voices and Documents. Edited, compiled, and annotated by Louis Menashe. Recorded at the Berkeley Campus of the University of California by Radio Station KPFA. 1966. Two 12-inch long-playing records. $19.96 for the set, plus $3.50 handling.

The twelve-page guide that accompanies these records provides background information and a chronology of the teach-in movement, excerpts from the speeches of some of the forty speakers who addressed the Berkeley audience,and suggested readings.

Speakers included Staughton Lynd, Aaron Wildavsky, Robert Scheer, Paul Potter, Paul Krassner, Bob Parris, Dr. Benjamin Spock, I.F. Stone,

M.S. Arnoni, Norman Mailer, Mario Savio, Dick Gregory, Senator Ernest Gruening, and Isaac Deutscher.

The historical importance of this two-record set lies not just in what it teaches listeners about the war in Vietnam, but also in what it demonstrates about the very medium of the teach-in itself: "a uniquely American form of politico-educational protest," says editor Menashe.

The *spoken word* section of the Folkways collection contains one Asia-related record:

The Original Read-in for Peace in Vietnam. Ed. Rosalind Wells and Louis Menashe. Produced by the Committee of the Professions. Recorded at Town Hall, New York, Feb. 20, 1966. One 12-inch long-playing record. $9.98, plus $3.50 handling.

The Town Hall read-in was "conceived as a cultural event," according to this record's editors, "an occasion for bearing witness to the viability of the American conscience, no less than as a political demonstration." "Like the teach-ins," they continue, "the read-in provides artists and writers with a novel platform for expressing concern and protest in the language they know best."

Writers and performing artists at the Town Hall event included Susan Sontag, Jules Feiffer, Tony Randall, Arthur Miller, Norman Mailer, Bernard Malamud, and Lillian Hellman. The eight-page guide that accompanies this record provides excerpts from the remarks of some of the twenty-nine personalities who spoke that night.

The Great Atlantic Radio Conspiracy, 2743 Maryland Ave., Baltimore, MD 21218. Tel: (301)243-6987. Order numbers are given in parentheses for each of the tapes listed below. All tapes are 30 minutes in length. Inquire for current price schedule. (Note: annotations are by the Great Atlantic Radio Conspiracy.)

The programs produced by this award-winning organization feature "political analysis and the radical arts." Great Atlantic radio programs "combine script, interviews, and music to present social commentary on issues of contemporary interest from a nonsectarian left and radical feminist point of view."

The conspiracy's audiotape collection, dating back to 1972, features open-reel and cassette tapes on subjects such as antinuclear poetry and music, the Arab-Israeli conflict, toxic wastes, and southern Africa.

Recent titles on Asia and the Pacific include:

American Involvement in South Korea. (22–980–297). September 1980.

"To protect corporate investments and maintain its military bases, the United States has supported a series of repressive dictatorships in South Korea. David Easter, an independent researcher for the American Friends Service Committee, and Wayne Brittenden, Southeast Asia correspondent for New Zealand Broadcasting, explore the reasons behind the continuing U.S. presence in South Korea today."

Battle for the Pacific. (30–484–408). April 1984.

"The Micronesian islands were placed in the care of the United States after World War II. The U.S. care has included blowing islands off the map with sixty-six nuclear bomb tests and displacing whole populations for military bases. Marshall Islander Darlene Keju and journalist Giff Johnson describe life on the islands under U.S. care and what Micronesians are doing about it: a nuclear-free constitution and resistance to the military on their islands."

Rewriting the History of the American War in Vietnam. (20–779–263) July 1979.

"Wars are always fought twice: first on the battlefields, then in the chronicles of historians. This is the story of the second battle of Vietnam. U.S. apologists are trying to win retrospectively by distorting the history students learn. Those who would rewrite this history know that our view of the past can determine our future."

Vietnam—The Music of Resistance. (20–779–264). July 1979.

"Music was a common bond for the antiwar movement. From Joan Baez to The Fugs, the songs of these musicians are as important today as ever. This program presents a musical documentary of resistance to the war in Vietnam."

Ladyslipper, P.O. Box 3130, Durham, NC 27705. Tel: (919) 683–1570 (for telephone charge card orders).

Ladyslipper is a nonprofit organization that has been involved in many facets of women's music since 1976. "Our basic purpose," its directors say, "has consistently been to heighten public awareness of the achievements of women artists and musicians and to expand the scope and availability of musical and literary recordings by women."

The 1985 edition of Ladyslipper's catalog and resource guide numbers sixty-four pages and contains listings of records, tapes, songbooks, and other musical resources in categories that range from punk to country, and from classical to reggae. The international category has many records and tapes from and about Latin America and Africa, but unfortunately, nothing on Asia and the Pacific.

Monitor Recordings, 156 Fifth Ave., New York, NY 10010. Tel: (212)989–2323. Order numbers are given in parentheses for each of the tapes listed below. Inquire for current price schedule.

Monitor has only a few records and tapes on the Asia and Pacific region and these are traditional in nature. These include seven recordings of the Bayanihan musical troupe from the Philippines, as well as these titles:

Flower Drum (Chinese Songs) (420; with text),
Shamim Ahmed: Ragas from India (489; instrumental),
Sounds and Music of China (525),
Vietnam Songs and Dances (731).

National Catholic Reporter Credence Cassettes, 115 E. Armour Blvd., P.O. Box 281, Kansas City, MO 64141. Tel: 1–800–821–7926 (for orders only).

Credence cassette tapes cover church-related topics such as liturgy, ministry, prayer, scripture, and spirituality. The "justice" category in the 1985 catalog contains tapes on nuclear war, Central America, nonviolence, and world hunger. There are no audiovisuals on the Asia and Pacific region.

Pacifica Radio Archive, 5316 Venice Blvd., Los Angeles, CA 90019. Tel:

(213) 931–1625. All programs are on cassette tape unless orders specify reel to reel. (Note: annotations are by the Pacifica Radio Archive.)

This radio archive boasts the oldest collection of public radio programing and "sound actualities" in the United States. A microfiche catalog of the twenty-thousand sound recordings made by Pacifica and independent producers since 1949 is available for $16, shipping and handling included. A catalog of Pacifica's most popular titles is also available (60 cents in stamps).

Recent titles on Asia and the Pacific include:

The Role of the CIA in Vietnam. Ronnie Lovler. 1983. 87′ cassette tape. $15. Pacifica catalog no. KZ1266.

"Keyes Beech, journalist, Frank Snepp, ex-CIA analyst, Ralph Mc Gehee, ex-CIA agent, and John Stockwell, ex-CIA agent, discuss the involvement of the CIA in Vietnam. Some of the panelists defend that role while others call for the disbandment of the agency. The panel was part of the University of Southern California Vietnam Reconsidered Conference, February 1983."

Women on the Global Assembly Line. Maggie Geddes and Mary Sinclair. 1981. 28′ cassette tape. $11. Pacifica catalog no. AZ0585.

"When multinational corporations set up factories in Hongkong and Mexico, they often hire women. Focusing on the electronics industry, this program explores why this is done and what the conditions are for the women working on assembly lines."

Women Unbound: The Role of Women in the People's Republic of China. Helene Rosenbluth and Eloise Klein Healy. 1982. 51′ cassette tape. $13. Pacifica catalog no. KZ1249.02.

"This program was produced from interviews with women in Shanghai, Nanjing, and Peking. They talk about how the lives of women are changing in modern China. The program is in Mandarin and English."

Paredon Records, P.O. Box 11260, Oakland, CA 94611. Tel: (415) 261–7015. Order numbers are given in parentheses for each of the records listed below. All entries below are 12-inch long-playing records. $8 each, plus postage and handling. (Note: annotations are from the Paredon catalog.)

For over ten years Paredon has been providing activists and educators with quality recordings of songs, music, poetry, and speeches about "class struggle, national liberation, women's emancipation, and democratic rights." Each Paredon album comes with a booklet giving full translations and historical, cultural, or political notes.

Records related to Asia and Pacific include:

The East Is Red. (P–1007). 3-record set. $24.

"The history of the Chinese people's revolution in epic ballad opera form. This world-renowned pageant is performed by more than three thousand workers, peasants, students, and soldiers in Peking."

The Legacy of Ho Chi Minh: Nothing Is More Precious Than Independence and Freedom. (P–1033).

"The writings, speeches, and poems of President Ho Chi Minh read in English by Vu Thien Dinh, leading member of the Association of Vietnamese Patriots in the United States, with music and songs about Ho Chi

Minh by peasants and professional musicians of Vietnam. Plus, Ho Chi Minh himself speaking in English to the American people."

Philippines: Bangon! Arise! (P–1029).

"Prepared as a joint project by cultural workers from the Preparatory Commission for the Union of Democratic Filipinos (KDP), this definitive collection of revolutionary songs spans the National Democratic struggle from 1896 to today, with the emphasis on songs currently playing a part in day-to-day political work in the liberated rural bases and in the urban underground movement [in the Philippines]."

Thailand: Songs for Life. Sung by Caravan. (P–1042).

"First recording available in the United States of songs from the peasant, student, and worker struggles for democratic rights in Thailand. Caravan was founded by students who helped spark the 1973 popular uprising against the military dictatorship. The content speaks of survival and revolution. The accompanying booklet has the Thai lyrics as well as English translations, historical, and political notes."

INFORMATION SOURCES

Third World Resource Directory: A Guide to Organizations and Publications. Edited by Thomas P. Fenton and Mary J. Heffron. Maryknoll, N.Y.: Orbis Books, 1984. 304pp. $17.95, plus $1.50 postage and handling. Illustrations, indexes. Available from Orbis Books, Maryknoll, NY 10545 or from Third World Resources, 464 19 St., Oakland, CA 94612.

The audiovisuals section (pp. 26–32) and the other resources section (pp. 33–36) of the Third World chapter are particularly important, but other chapters—such as the ones on women and on human rights—should be consulted as well.

Third World Resources: A Quarterly Review of Resources from and about the Third World. 4 issues/year. Newsletter. 28cm. 16pp. $25/year (organizational subscription), $25/two years (individual subscription). Subscriptions are available on a calendar-year basis only.

This quarterly newsletter contains critical review notices of newly released educational and action resources from and about the Third World. In addition, each issue contains a four-page pullout with a complete and up-to-date compilation of resources on one particular region or issue.

6

Other Resources

This chapter is divided into three sections: crafts and products; curriculum guides and materials; and news services.

CRAFTS AND PRODUCTS

The following organizations offer crafts and products for sale from various parts of the Third World. Write to them for their catalogs.

Friends of the Third World, 611 W. Wayne St., Fort Wayne, IN 46802. Tel: (219) 422-6821.

Jubilee Crafts, 300 W. Apsley, Philadelphia, PA 19144. Tel: (215) 849-0808.

New Society Products, 853 Broadway, Suite 1105, New York, NY 10003. Tel: (212) 254-0853.

Northern Sun Merchandising, 2736 Lyndale Ave. S., Minneapolis, MN 55408. Tel: (612) 874-6409.

Pueblo to People, 5218 Chenevert, Rm. 1013, Houston, TX 77004. Tel: (713) 523-1197.

Third World Handarts, 1618 N. French St., Santa Ana, CA 92701. Tel: (714) 835-8760.

CURRICULUM GUIDES AND MATERIALS

The **Committee on Teaching about Asia,** a standing committee of the Association of Asian Studies, aims to further the understanding of Asia by improving the teaching of Asian studies at the elementary, secondary, and undergraduate levels. The CTA publishes a quarterly newsletter, *CTA Newsletter,* that contains valuable curriculum suggestions and reviews of materials. Write: c/o Urban Education Program, 420 W. Wrightwood, Chicago, IL 60614. Tel: (312) 929-4246.

Another good source of curriculum materials on Asia and the Pacific is

AMIE, Inc., 5539 N. Lakewood, Chicago, IL 60640. Tel: (312) 769–3295. Write for their catalog of print and visual materials on India, Nepal, Sri Lanka, China, Vietnam, Malaysia, and other regions.

The following are noteworthy curriculum guides and materials:

Chang, Michael, and Bing Shaw. ***Resource List for Teaching about China.*** New York: Global Perspectives Information Exchange Network, October 1984. 12pp. Free. Available either from Global Perspectives in Education, 218 E. 18 St., New York, NY 10003 or from the SPICE China Project at Stanford University (see p. 110 below).

This hand guide brings together information on curriculum and media guides, periodicals, travel opportunities, background readings, outreach activites of the East Asian Resource Center, and many more aspects of China-related education.

Friendship Press. ***Showcase Suitcase: Korea.*** New York: Friendship Press, 1984. $28.95.

Friendship Press prepared this collection of Christian educational resources for the 1984–85 Interdenominational Mission Study on Korea. The set includes three volumes for adults and three for children. In addition, there is a four-color wall map (23 × 35inches) that uses the Peters Projection to depict the geography of Korea and surrounding lands.

Indochina Curriculum Group. ***The Vietnam Era: A Guide to Teaching Resources.*** Cambridge, Mass.: Indochina Curriculum Groups, 1978. 105pp. $5. Photographs, illustrations, maps, appendixes, title index.

The Vietnam Era, compiled by a collective of high-school teachers and writers in the Boston area, seeks to provide viewpoints other than those normally found in history textbooks dealing with the war in Indochina and to encourage critical evaluation of teaching materials on the war. The revised edition planned for 1982 was never done, but the 1978 edition stands the test of time.

McGinnis, James, et al. ***Education for Peace and Justice.*** Vol. II: *Global Dimensions.* St. Louis: Institute for Peace and Justice, 1984. 324pp. $14.25. Maps, illustrations resource list, bibliography.

This curriculum guide contains a case study on the Philippines that deals with the "conflict between the short-term (at least) U.S. security interests and human rights."

The authors give students three policy options to evaluate and vote on, as if they were members of the U.S. House of Representatives. They are then offered a variety of possibilities for action.

The case study provides background information on the Philippines, personal stories about two Filipinos, resources for further study and action, and readings from the *Congressional Record* and *St. Louis Post-Dispatch.*

Martin, Roberta. ***Contemporary China: A Teaching Workbook.*** New York: Columbia University, East Asian Curriculum Project, 1983. Rev. ed. 410pp. $29. Available from the Social Studies School Service. Looseleaf, 8.5 × 11 inches. Photographs, film guides, outline map, two forty-page booklets, illustrations, time line, reproducible student units, resources.

Among the topics covered in this attractive curriculum are U.S.-China relations, language, art, culture, geography, and the history of traditional and revolutionary China.

Oxfam Education Unit. ***Samanyaya School: An Indian Community School.*** Oxford, England: Oxfam Education Unit, 1977. $10. Available in North America from Oxfam America (Boston, Mass.).

The story of a village and a Ghandian school in one of the poorest parts of India, Bihar State. The multimedia kit illustrates some of the problems of change and development facing Indian society today. Recommended for junior high and high school level students, the packet includes information about the socioeconomic characteristics of the community, many black and white photographs, 28 color slides, and a record of music from the Samanyay school.

Social Studies School Service. 1985 Catalog. Culver City, Calif.: Social Studies School Service, 1985. 274pp. Free.

This well-designed catalog is a gold mine of educational materials for the social studies teacher. Subject areas include world history and geography, area studies, the arms race and nuclear war, global education, and more. Materials include paperbacks, multimedia kits, videocassettes, computer software, reproducible spirit masters, simulations, and a variety of other teaching tools. All of the items are available directly from the Social Studies School Service, many of them with quantity discounts.

Stanford Program on International and Cross-Cultural Education (SPICE). ***Catalogue of Materials.*** Stanford, Calif.: SPICE, 1985. 17pp. Free.

This guide to curriculum materials available from the SPICE program at Stanford University covers two Asia-related projects: China and Japan.

The China project (the only one that falls within the scope of our definition of the Third World) has produced three noteworthy guides:

1. ***Bay Area Resources on China.*** This fifty-eight-page guide contains listings of a broad spectrum of resources: written and audiovisuals aids, academic institutions, libraries, museums, private and public outlets with classroom materials on China, and so forth. The guide is designed with California Bay Area teachers in mind. $3.50.

2. ***Teaching about China: Cultural Expressions.*** See p. 36 above.

3. ***Teaching about China: People and Daily Life.*** See p. 36 above.

U.S.-China People's Friendship Association, Center for Teaching about China. ***China in the Classroom: Resources from the Center for Teaching about China.*** Washington, D.C.: USCPFA, Center for Teaching about China. 1984. 22pp. Free.

This illustrated guide covers references/guides; books for elementary, intermediate, and secondary school levels; activity books, maps, and charts; biographies; background readings on a variety of themes such as history and economy; magazines; filmstrips and slideshows; and a special section of supplemental low-cost materials.

Items are well-annotated and are all available directly from the Center for Teaching about China.

Wien, Barbara J., ed. ***Peace and World Order Studies: A Curriculum Guide.*** New York: World Policy Institute, 1984. 4th ed. 741pp. $14.95. Resources, bibliography.

This guide contains over one hundred course syllabi and outlines (e.g., "America and Vietnam" by George Lopez of Earlham College, and "Peace in the Southern Philippines" by Robert McAmis of Mindanao State University) drawn from a wide variety of disciplines, including political science, literature, international law, and the natural sciences. There are fourteen subject divisions such as human rights and social justice, world political economy and economic justice, and regional studies.

In addition to the course outlines, *Peace and World Order Studies* contains a valuable five-part section of resources: funding sources; filmography; periodicals and journals; organizations; and bibliography.

For additional information on curriculum guides and materials see the catalogs, directories, and guides section above (pp. 37–40), contact the outreach coordinator at the university centers listed in appendix 1, and consult these publications from Third World Resources:

Third World Resource Directory: A Guide to Organizations and Publications. Edited by Thomas P. Fenton and Mary J. Heffron. Maryknoll, N.Y.: Orbis Books, 1984. 304pp. $17.95, plus $1.50 postage and handling. Illustrations, indexes. Available from Orbis Books, Maryknoll, NY 10545, or from Third World Resources, 464 19 St., Oakland, CA 94612.

The other resources sections of the Third World chapter (pp. 33–39) and the chapter on Asia and the Pacific (pp. 86–88) are particularly important, though other chapters—such as the ones on women and on human rights—should be consulted as well.

Third World Resources: A Quarterly Review of Resources from and about the Third World. 4 issues/year. Newsletter. 28cm. 16pp. $25/year (organizational subscription), $25/two years (individual subscription). Subscriptions are available on a calendar-year basis only. Available from Third World Resources, 464 19 St., Oakland, CA 94612.

This quarterly newsletter contains critical reviews of newly released educational and action-related resources from and about the Third World. In addition, each issue contains a four-page pullout with a complete and up-to-date compilation of resources on one particular region or issue.

NEWS SERVICES

Clipping Services

Asia Monitor Resource Center, 444–46 Nathan Rd., 8–B, Kowloon, Hongkong. Tel: (3)855319.

AMRC has access to numerous newspapers and magazines from the entire Asia and Pacific regions and is willing to provide a customized clipping service on any of the political and economic issues with which the center is concerned. Contact the center for details.

Note also that all of the periodical clippings used in the compilation of the center's publication, *Asia Labour Monitor* (as well as its predecessor, *Asia Monitor*), are kept on file and are retrievable using the reference codes that accompany each entry in the magazines. Inquire for fees.

Data Center, 464 19 St., Oakland, CA 94612. Tel: (415) 835–4692.

The Data Center receives over four hundred national and international newspapers and magazines representing a variety of political opinions. The center's staff will monitor and clip articles from these periodicals on regions or issues related to Asia and the Pacific and provide full-text photocopies on a regular basis. Call or write for a free estimate.

Korean Resource Center, 1720 Oregon St., No. 10, Berkeley, CA 94703. Tel: (415) 486–8759.

Since May 1984 the Korean Resource Center has been packaging clippings on Korea received from fifty-seven periodicals clipped by the Data Center and offering them to subscribers for $6/month. Periodicals include nine major newspapers and magazines such as *Far Eastern Economic Review, Fortune, Progressive* and *World Press Review.*

North American Coalition for Human Rights in Korea, 110 Maryland Ave., NE, Washington, DC 20002. Tel: (202) 546–4304.

The coalition's Human Rights Data Packet (formerly Key Contact) includes translated documents, news clipping, brief analysis of current developments in the human rights situation in Korea, and policy and action recommendations. The monthly twenty-page packet costs $20/year.

Press Services

Asia-Pacific People's Environment Network, c/o Sahabat Alam Malaysia, 37, Lorong Birch, Penang, West Malaysia. Tel: 376930.

Sahabat Alam Malaysia (Friends of the Earth) has inaugurated a press service that distributes two feature-length articles once every two weeks on a wide range of environmental subjects such as pesticides, nuclear energy, pollution, wildlife, forestry, fisheries, and toxic wastes. "APPEN Features" and "SAM Features" are available for an annual $80 subscription, plus a donation upon publication of any of the articles.

Telephone Hotlines

Crisis in Korea is a monthly thirty-minute radio program prepared by the Committee for a New Korea Policy and provided free to radio stations across the country. Sample tapes are available to individuals for promotional use. Contact: Committee for a New Korea Policy.

Korea-Phone is a taped phone message offering a weekly summary of recent events in Korea. The tape is updated every Tuesday by the North American Coalition for Human Rights in Korea (Washington, D.C.). Call (202) 546-NEWS. The coalition offers a transcript of "Korea-Phone" for $10/year or 50 cents/week.

Appendixes

1. UNIVERSITY CENTERS WITH ASIA AND PACIFIC PROGRAMS

Consult the following two directories for information on colleges and universities in North America that have studies programs focused on Asia and the Pacific:

Directory of Area Studies on U.S. and Canadian Campuses. New York: Academy for Educational Development, World Studies Data Bank, annual.

Foreign Area Programs at North American Universities: A Directory. Claremont, Calif.: California Institute of Public Affairs, 1979.

These North American universities are notable for their Asia and Pacific studies programs and for their educational outreach activities regarding the area:

Columbia University, East Asian Institute and **Southern Asian Institute,** 420 W. 118 St., New York, NY 10027. Tel: (212) 280–4278 & 4462.

Cornell University, Southeast Asia Program, 120 Uris Hall, Ithaca, NY 14853. Tel: (607) 256–2378.

Indiana University, Asian Studies Research Institute, Bloomington, IN 47405. Tel: (812) 337–1605.

McGill University, Centre for Developing Area Studies, Montreal, Quebec H3A 2T7, Canada. Tel: (514) 392–5321.

Michigan State University, Asian Studies Center, c/o Center for International Studies, #101, East Lansing, MI 48824. Tel: (517) 353–1680.

New York University, Asian Studies Curriculum Center, 635 East Bldg., Washington Sq., New York, NY 10003. Tel: (212) 598–2785.

Ohio State University, School and Community Outreach Program on Asia, 308 Dulles Hall, 230 W. 17 Ave., Columbus, OH 43210. Tel: (614) 422-9660, ext. 3838.

Stanford University, BAYCEP and SPICE, Lou Henry Hoover Bldg., Rm. 200, Stanford, CA 94305. Tel: (415) 497-1114.

University of Arizona, Dept. of Oriental Studies, Tucson, AZ 85721. Tel: (602) 626-5463.

University of California—Santa Cruz, Center for South Pacific Studies, Santa Cruz, CA 95064. Tel: (408) 429-2191.

University of Chicago, Chicago East Asian Resource and Education Center, Kelly Hall, Rm. 403, 5848 University Ave., Chicago, IL 60637. Tel: (312) 753-2632.

University of Illinois, Center for Asian Studies, 1208 W. California Ave., Urbana, IL 61801. Tel: (217) 333-4850, ext. 0451.

University of Michigan, East Asian Studies Center, 104 Lane Hall, Ann Arbor, MI 48109. Tel: (313) 764-5109.

University of Texas, Center for Asian Studies, Texas Program for Educational Resources on Asia, Austin, TX 78712. Tel: (512) 471-5811.

University of Toronto, Centre for International Studies, Toronto, Ontario M5S 1H8, Canada. Tel: (416) 978-3350.

University of Washington, East Asia Resource Center, School of International Studies, Seattle, WA 98195. Tel: (206) 543-1921.

University of Wisconsin—Madison, Southern Asian Studies Center, 1244 Van Hise Hall, Madison, WI 53706. Tel: (608) 262-3012.

Yale University, Council on East Asian Studies, 85 Trumbell St., P.O. Box 13A, New Haven, CT 06520. Tel: (203) 432-4029.

2. CHRISTIAN CHURCHES WITH ASIA AND PACIFIC OFFICES

For information on churches in North America, see the ***Yearbook of American and Canadian Churches***, prepared and edited in the Office of Research, Evaluation, and Planning of the National Council of Churches (USA), 475 Riverside Dr., New York, NY 10115. The 1984 edition was edited by Constant H. Jacquet, Jr. (Nashville, Tenn.: Abingdon Press, 1984. 298pp.).

For names and addresses of national councils of churches in Asia and the Pacific, see the ***Directory of Christian Councils***, published by the World Council of Churches, 150 Route de Ferney, 1211 Geneva 20, Switzerland. The third edition of this directory appeared in 1980. The *Yearbook of American and Canadian Churches* (see above) provides an abbreviated list of Asian and Pacific councils on pages 159–60 in the 1984 edition.

Consult the ***Official Catholic Directory*** for names, addresses, and telephone numbers of North American Roman Catholic missionary organizations with personnel in Asia and the Pacific.

The following national church offices have Asia divisions or liaison secretaries.

Canada

Anglican Church of Canada, Church House, 600 Jarvis St., Toronto, Ontario M4Y 2J6, Canada. Tel: (416) 924–9192.

Canadian Conference of Catholic Bishops, 90 Parent Ave., Ottawa, Ontario K1N 7B1, Canada. Tel: (613) 236–9461.

United Church of Canada, Division of World Outreach, Asia and the Pacific, 85 St. Clair Ave. E., Toronto, Ontario M4T 1M8, Canada. Tel: (416) 925–5931.

United States

National Council of Churches (USA), Division of Overseas Ministries, 475 Riverside Dr., New York, NY 10115–0050. Tel: (212) 870–2371. Areas of focus: Southern Asia; Committee for East Asia and the Pacific (including the China Program, Micronesia Coalition, and Japan and Hongkong).

United States Catholic Conference, Social Development and World Peace, European, East Asian, and Political Issues Office, 1312 Massachusetts Ave., NW, Washington, DC 20005. Tel: (202) 659–6600.

American Baptist Churches in the USA, Board of International Ministries, Valley Forge, PA 19482. Tel: (215) 768–2000. Area secretaries: East Asia; South Asia.

Christian Church (Disciples of Christ), Division of Overseas Ministries, P.O. Box 1986, Indianapolis, IN 46206. Tel: (317) 353–1491. Departments: Southeast Asia; East Asia and the Pacific; Southern Asia.

Church of the Brethren, World Ministries Commission, 1451 Dundee Ave., Elgin, IL 60120. Tel: (312) 742–5100.

Episcopal Church, World Mission in Church and Society, 815 Second Ave., New York, NY 10017. Tel: (212) 867–8400.

Lutheran Church in America, Division for World Mission and Ecumenism, 231 Madison Ave., New York, NY 10016. Tel: (212) 696–6700.

Mennonite Central Committee, 21 S. 12 St., Akron, PA 17501. Tel: (717) 859–1151 and 201–1483 Pembina Hwy., Winnepeg, MB R3T 2C8, Canada.

Presbyterian Church (USA), 475 Riverside Dr., New York, NY 10115. Tel: (212) 870–2005. Area liaisons: Southeast Asia/Pacific; South Asia/China/Hongkong, Taiwan.

Reformed Church in America, 475 Riverside Dr., New York, NY 10115. Tel: (212) 870–2841.

United Church of Christ, Board for World Ministries, 475 Riverside Dr., New York, NY 10115. Tel: (212) 870–2831. Regional secretaries: SouthernAsia; Pacific.

United Methodist Church, Board of Global Ministries, World Division, 475 Riverside Dr., New York, NY 10115. Tel: (212) 870–3600.

3. CHINA PROGRAMS

Churches

Canada China Programme Canada Chine, c/o Canadian Council of Churches, 40 St. Clair Ave. E., Toronto, Ontario M4T 1M9, Canada. Tel: (416) 921–4152.

China Program, National Council of Churches (USA), Division of Overseas Ministries, 475 Riverside Dr., Rm. 616, New York, NY 10115. Tel: (212) 870–2371.

US–China Peoples Friendship Association Offices

National: Center for Teaching about China, 2025 Eye St., NW, Suite 715, Washington, DC 20006. Tel: (202) 296–4147.

East: 720 Massachusetts Ave., Cambridge, MA 02139. Tel: (617) 491–0577.

Midwest: 5555 N. Sheridan, Rm. 806, Chicago, IL 60640. Tel: (312) 275–4440.

South: 100 Edgewood Ave., NE, Rm. 1026, Atlanta, GA 30303. Tel: (404) 659–3613.

West: 50 Oak St., Rm. 502, San Francisco, CA 94102. Tel: (415) 863–0537.

For a list of the regional China councils of the Asia Society, contact the **Asia Society, China Council**, 1785 Massachusetts Ave., NW, Washington, DC 20036.

Indexes

ORGANIZATIONS

This index contains the names of all organizations associated with the production and/or distribution of resources included in this directory. See the Subjects Index below for references to organizations not directly connected to those resources. Page numbers in boldface signify that the organization's address will be found in the text. If a resource is easily available at a library or bookstore the publisher's address is not given.

INDIVIDUALS

This index contains the names of all individuals associated with the production of resources included in this directory.

TITLES

This index contains the names of all the print and audiovisual resources included in this directory. The distributor's address appears either in the text or in the Organizations Index when we have judged that the resource is not easily available through a library or bookstore.

GEOGRAPHICAL AREAS

This index includes all references to countries and regions specific to Asia and the Pacific. Names are given as they appear in the resource and imply no political judgment about the legitimacy of national claims. Regional references (e.g., Southeast Asia) are given only when there is a resource that treats the area as a whole. Country references are provided only for those organizations in chapter 1 that specify a concern for the particular country.

SUBJECTS

This topical index also contains references to organizations not directly related to the production or distribution of resources listed in this directory. Keyword descriptions for the issue-focus of organizations in chapter 1 do not appear in this index.

Third World Resources

464 19th Street Oakland, CA 94612

Third World Resources gathers, catalogs, annotates, and publicizes education and action resources from and about the Third World.

Resource Directories

Twelve directories are being compiled on these subjects:

- Third World general
- Africa
- Asia & Pacific
- Latin America & Caribbean
- Middle East
- Women in the Third World
- Food, hunger, agribusiness
- Human rights
- Militarism, peace, disarmament
- Native peoples & natural resources
- Nuclear arms & energy
- TNCs & labor

Quarterly Newsletter

The *Third World Resources* newsletter contains notices and descriptive listings of organizations and newly released print, audiovisual, and other educational resources on Third World regions and issues. Inquire for subscription rates. Sample copy: US $1.

Each 16-page issue contains a unique 4-page insert with a comprehensive listing of resources on one particular region or subject. Inquire about discounts for bulk purchases.

Documentation Center

All resources are cataloged and integrated into the library collection of the Data Center where they are accessible to Center library users and Search Service clients. Bibliographical data are stored in a computerized data base to facilitate identification and retrieval of cross-referenced resources.

Third World Resources is a financially independent project of the Data Center, a non-profit, tax-exempt (501.c.3) resource center. Contributions to Third World Resources are tax-deductible.

THIRD WORLD RESOURCES

A QUARTERLY REVIEW OF RESOURCES FROM & ABOUT THE THIRD WORLD

Keep the invaluable information in this resource directory complete, correct, and up-to-date by subscribing to *Third World Resources* (ISSN 8755-8831).

Third World Resources provides descriptions and capsule reviews of organizations, books, periodicals, pamphlets, audiovisual, and other education and action resources on Third World regions and issues. Entries include complete ordering information and are indexed annually. The Editors' Notes column contains updates and corrections of information published in each of the resource directories in the 12-volume set.

Each issue of the 16-page newsletter contains a unique 4-page pullout with comprehensive listings of resources on one Third World region or issue. Available at bulk discounts, these 4-page guides are excellent inexpensive handouts for talks, workshops, and study programs.

ORDER FORM

Newsletter Subscription Form

☐ Please enter my subscription to Third World Resources at this rate:
U.S. and Canada: ___ Organizational ($25/year) or ___ Individual ($25/two years)
Foreign Airmail: ___ Organizational ($35/year) or ___ Individual ($40/two years)
Note: Subscriptions run on a calendar-year basis only. Individual subscribers will receive a prorated refund if they decide to cancel at the end of the first year.

☐ Please send a sample copy of *Third World Resources* ($2).

Third World Resource Directory

☐ Please send _____ copy/copies of the *Third World Resource Directory: A Guide to Organizations and Publications.* Compiled and edited by Thomas P. Fenton and Mary J. Heffron. Maryknoll, N.Y.: Orbis Books, 1984, 304pp. $17.95. Add (per copy): $1.50 for postage in North America; $2.50 for book rate postage overseas; $6 for airmail overseas.

☐ Enclosed is information on our organization for inclusion in future resource directories or the *Third World Resources* newsletter.

☐ Please add my/our name to your mailing list.

NAME ______________________________

ADDRESS ______________________________

____

____

Enclosed is US$ __________ for the materials I/we ordered above. Please make check/money order payable in U.S. dollars to **Third World Resources** and send to 464 19th Street, Oakland, CA 94612 USA.

ORDER FORM

Newsletter Subscription Form

☐ Please enter my subscription to Third World Resources at this rate:
U.S. and Canada: ___ Organizational ($25/year) or ___ Individual ($25/two years)
Foreign Airmail: ___ Organizational ($35/year) or ___ Individual ($40/two years)
Note: Subscriptions run on a calendar-year basis only. Individual subscribers will receive a prorated refund if they decide to cancel at the end of the first year.

☐ Please send a sample copy of *Third World Resources* ($2).

Third World Resource Directory

☐ Please send _____ copy/copies of the *Third World Resource Directory: A Guide to Organizations and Publications.* Compiled and edited by Thomas P. Fenton and Mary J. Heffron. Maryknoll, N.Y.: Orbis Books, 1984, 304pp. $17.95. Add (per copy): $1.50 for postage in North America; $2.50 for book rate postage overseas; $6 for airmail overseas.

☐ Enclosed is information on our organization for inclusion in future resource directories or the *Third World Resources* newsletter.

☐ Please add my/our name to your mailing list.

NAME ______________________________

ADDRESS ______________________________

____

____

Enclosed is US$ __________ for the materials I/we ordered above. Please make check/money order payable in U.S. dollars to **Third World Resources** and send to 464 19th Street, Oakland, CA 94612 USA.